The definitive guide to the leading employers
recruiting graduates during 2012-2013.

HIGH FLIERS PUBLICATIONS LTD
IN ASSOCIATION WITH THE TIMES

Published by High Fliers Publications Limited
King's Gate, 1 Bravingtons Walk, London N1 9AE
Telephone: 020 7428 9100   *Web:* www.Top100GraduateEmployers.com

Editor Martin Birchall
Publisher Gill Thomas
Production Manager Robin Burrows
Production Assistant Grace Proctor
Portrait Photography Sarah Merson

The Times Top 100 Graduate Employers is based on research results
from *The UK Graduate Careers Survey 2012*, produced by High Fliers
Research Ltd.

The greatest care has been taken in compiling this book. However, no
responsibility can be accepted by the publishers or compilers for the
accuracy of the information presented.

Where opinion is expressed it is that of the author or advertiser and
does not necessarily coincide with the editorial views of High Fliers
Publications Limited or *The Times* newspaper.

Printed and bound in Italy by L.E.G.O. S.p.A.

A CIP catalogue record for this book
is available from the British Library.
ISBN 978-0-9559257-3-3

Contents

Foreword

By **Martin Birchall**
Editor, *The Times Top 100 Graduate Employers*

Welcome to the brand new edition of *The Times Top 100 Graduate Employers*, your guide to the UK's leading employers who are recruiting graduates in 2012-2013.

The view across the City of London has been a troubled one for much of 2012 with the banking sector embroiled in the Libor interest rate-fixing scandal, accusations of money-laundering, fierce rows over bankers' pay, the continuing Euro crisis, and the UK's slide back into recession for the second time in less than five years.

But despite the grim headlines, the City's leading banks and financial institutions recruited more than 3,500 new graduates in 2012 and are planning to hire even more in the next twelve months.

There is no doubt that the double-dip recession in the wider UK economy has had a profound effect on graduates and the general employment market. Official figures show that just 49 per cent of those who left university in 2011 were in full-time employment six months after graduation and tens of thousands of those who did find work were employed in non-graduate roles.

For many of Britain's most successful employers, however, recruiting new graduates has always been about developing a steady supply of future managers and leaders for their organisation, rather than simply filling immediate vacancies. So even during the worst of the original recession in 2008 and 2009, very few top employers were keen to break this essential talent pipeline and the vast majority of organisations opted not to shut down their graduate programmes.

Across the UK, an estimated five thousand employers are preparing to recruit graduates in the year ahead.

This commitment to maintaining recruitment has helped the graduate job market recover more quickly than other parts of the economy – the number of vacancies available for university-leavers increased sharply in 2010 and rose again in 2011, restoring almost 90 per cent of the graduate roles that were cancelled or left unfilled at the beginning of the downturn. And even with the UK back in recession again in 2012, the number of graduate vacancies available increased slightly year-on-year.

&& Across the UK, an estimated five thousand employers are preparing to recruit graduates in the year ahead. &&

The latest research shows that confidence is continuing to improve on university campuses too. Final year students from the 'Class of 2012' made an unprecedented number of applications to graduate employers during their job hunting – 40 per cent more than just two years ago – and a record proportion of finalists started their careers research in the first or second year of their studies, determined to get ahead in the graduate job market.

If you're one of the 340,000 finalists due to graduate in the summer of 2013, then the outlook is also encouraging. Employers featured within this edition of *The Times Top 100 Graduate Employers* expect to increase their graduate intake by a further 7.2 per cent during the 2012-2013 recruitment season.

Across the UK, an estimated five thousand employers are preparing to recruit graduates in the year ahead and more than six hundred organisations have already confirmed that they will be holding recruitment events on campus. With such a wide choice of different types of employment and graduate jobs, how then can prospective employers be assessed and ranked?

To find out, we interviewed 17,737 final year students who graduated from universities across the UK in the summer of 2012, and asked them "Which employer do you think offers the best opportunities for graduates?". Between them, the 'Class of 2012' named organisations in every imaginable employment sector – the country's best-known retailers, top City investment banks,

leading charities, management consulting firms, Government departments, and the 'Big Four' accounting & professional services firms. The one hundred employers who were mentioned most often during the research form *The Times Top 100 Graduate Employers*.

This book is therefore a celebration of the employers who are judged to offer the brightest prospects for graduates. Whether by the perceived quality of their training programmes, the business success that they enjoy, the scale of their organisations, or by the impression that their recruitment promotions have made – these are the employers that are most attractive to university-leavers in 2012.

The Times Top 100 Graduate Employers won't necessarily identify which organisation is right for you – only you can decide that. But it is an invaluable reference if you want to discover what Britain's leading employers have to offer.

Leaving university and finding your first job can be a daunting process but it is one of the most important steps you'll ever take. Having a thorough understanding of the range of opportunities available must be a good way to start.

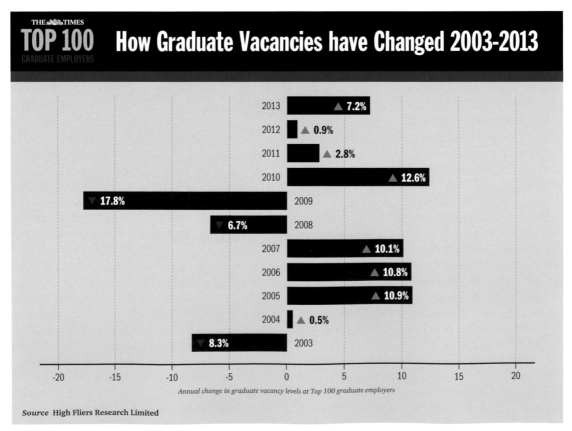

THE TIMES TOP 100 GRADUATE EMPLOYERS — How Graduate Vacancies have Changed 2003-2013

Year	Change
2013	▲ 7.2%
2012	▲ 0.9%
2011	▲ 2.8%
2010	▲ 12.6%
2009	▼ 17.8%
2008	▼ 6.7%
2007	▲ 10.1%
2006	▲ 10.8%
2005	▲ 10.9%
2004	▲ 0.5%
2003	▼ 8.3%

Annual change in graduate vacancy levels at Top 100 graduate employers

Source High Fliers Research Limited

The thing that takes
you further than
a lilo in a hotel pool.

We want it.

The kind of person you are really determines
if you can make it onto one of the most
challenging, rewarding and sought-after
graduate training programmes in the UK.
Qualifications are important, but determination,
competitiveness and team skills are vital. Within
a few months you could be managing three to
four Aldi stores, so you'll also need to be able
to take on real responsibility. If you're motivated
and ambitious, then you never know; one day
you might wake up realising you've landed
a career that is second to none.

**Graduate Area Manager £40,000
rising to £63,500 after 4 years.**

**Fully expensed Audi A4.
Opportunity for directorship within 5 years.
International secondment opportunities.**

aldirecruitment.co.uk/tt100

 Apply yourself here.

KPMG
cutting through complexity

Do you want it sugar coated or straight up?

Graduate careers in
Audit, Tax and Advisory

kpmg.co.uk/times100

Compiling the Top 100 Graduate Employers

By **Gill Thomas**
Publisher, High Fliers Publications

Britain may have plunged into recession twice in less than five years, but the graduate job market is continuing to hold its own and an estimated five thousand employers, large and small, will be hiring graduates from UK universities during the 2012-2013 recruitment season.

With such a wide choice of employment to choose from, selecting the organisation that is 'right' for you can be quite a challenge. How can you evaluate the different opportunities and decide which employers offer the best career paths? What basis can you use to assess so many different organisations and jobs?

It's clear there are no simple answers to these questions and no single individual employer can ever hope to be right for every graduate – everyone makes their own judgement about the organisations they want to work for and the type of job they find the most attractive.

How then can anyone produce a meaningful league table of Britain's leading graduate employers? What criteria can define whether one organisation is 'better' than another? To compile the new edition of *The Times Top 100 Graduate Employers*, the independent market research company, High Fliers Research, interviewed 17,737 final year students who left UK universities in the summer of 2012.

These finalists from the 'Class of 2012' who took part in the study were selected at random to represent the full cross-section of finalists at their universities, not just those who had already secured graduate employment. The research examined students' experiences during their search for a graduate job and asked them about their attitudes to employers.

> *"An estimated five thousand employers will be hiring graduates from UK universities during the 2012-2013 recruitment season."*

The key question used to produce the *Top 100* was "Which employer do you think offers the best opportunities for graduates?" This question was deliberately open-ended and students were not prompted in any way. Across the whole survey, finalists mentioned more than 1,100 different organisations – from the smallest local employers, to some of the world's best-known companies. The responses were analysed to identify the number of times each employer was mentioned. The one hundred organisations that were mentioned most often are the *The Times Top 100 Graduate Employers* for 2012.

Looking at the considerable selection of answers given by finalists from the 'Class of 2012', it is clear that individual students used several different criteria to determine which employer

THE TIMES TOP 100 GRADUATE EMPLOYERS

The Times Top 100 Graduate Employers 2012

	2011			2011	
1.	1	PWC	51.	52	NETWORK RAIL
2.	2	DELOITTE	52.	57	FRESHFIELDS BRUCKHAUS DERINGER
3.	3	KPMG	53.	61	ATKINS
4.	7	TEACH FIRST	54.	56	CREDIT SUISSE
5.	4	ALDI	55.	71	MCDONALD'S
6.	5	NHS	56.	NEW	EUROPEAN COMMISSION
7.	8	CIVIL SERVICE	57.	67	BAIN & COMPANY
8.	10	ERNST & YOUNG	58.	75	CO-OPERATIVE GROUP
9.	6	BBC	59.	64	DLA PIPER
10.	11	JOHN LEWIS PARTNERSHIP	60.	40	MARS
11.	9	ACCENTURE	61.	46	UBS
12.	20	TESCO	62.	89	SANTANDER
13.	12	HSBC	63.	62	BOOTS
14.	21	GOOGLE	64.	79	ASDA
15.	13	GOLDMAN SACHS	65.	77	BOSTON CONSULTING GROUP
16.	14	BARCLAYS	66.	98	NUCLEARGRADUATES
17.	16	BP	67.	74	BANK OF AMERICA MERRILL LYNCH
18.	15	GLAXOSMITHKLINE	68.	80	BLOOMBERG
19.	24	UNILEVER	69.	43	CENTRICA
20.	23	J.P. MORGAN	70.	49	LOCAL GOVERNMENT
21.	18	PROCTER & GAMBLE	71.	51	ARCADIA GROUP
22.	17	ROYAL BANK OF SCOTLAND GROUP	72.	65	ROYAL NAVY
23.	22	ARMY	73.	70	HERBERT SMITH
24.	19	IBM	74.	72	FOREIGN AND COMMONWEALTH OFFICE
25.	26	ROLLS-ROYCE	75.	90	PENGUIN
26.	60	JAGUAR LAND ROVER	76.	39	CANCER RESEARCH UK
27.	53	APPLE	77.	47	EXXONMOBIL
28.	27	MARKS & SPENCER	78.	NEW	BRITISH AIRWAYS
29.	28	BARCLAYS INVESTMENT BANK (FORMERLY BARCLAYS CAPITAL)	79.	68	POLICE
30.	25	L'ORÉAL	80.	NEW	TOWERS WATSON
31.	29	ALLEN & OVERY	81.	58	SAATCHI & SAATCHI
32.	38	LIDL	82.	78	TRANSPORT FOR LONDON
33.	48	MICROSOFT	83.	84	DIAGEO
34.	34	MORGAN STANLEY	84.	95	NATIONAL GRID
35.	31	SHELL	85.	NEW	NORTON ROSE
36.	30	BAE SYSTEMS	86.	63	OXFAM
37.	37	ARUP	87.	73	AIRBUS
38.	32	LLOYDS BANKING GROUP	88.	81	GRANT THORNTON
39.	33	SAINSBURY'S	89.	88	SAVILLS
40.	35	MCKINSEY & COMPANY	90.	NEW	GE
41.	41	SKY	91.	87	E.ON
42.	50	WPP	92.	NEW	BRITISH SUGAR
43.	42	LINKLATERS	93.	69	ROYAL AIR FORCE
44.	59	CITI	94.	85	OLIVER WYMAN
45.	36	CLIFFORD CHANCE	95.	NEW	LLOYD'S
46.	45	BT	96.	82	EDF ENERGY
47.	91	NESTLÉ	97.	86	KRAFT FOODS
48.	55	DEUTSCHE BANK	98.	NEW	BDO
49.	44	SLAUGHTER AND MAY	99.	NEW	DEPARTMENT FOR INTERNATIONAL DEVELOPMENT
50.	54	MI5 – THE SECURITY SERVICE	100.	99	HOGAN LOVELLS

Source **High Fliers Research** 17,737 final year students leaving UK universities in the summer of 2012 were asked the open-ended question 'Which employer do you think offers the best opportunities for graduates?' during interviews for *The UK Graduate Careers Survey 2012*

they considered offered the best opportunities for graduates. Some focused on employers' general reputations – their public image, their business profile or their commercial success.

Others evaluated employers based on the information they had seen during their job search – the quality of recruitment promotions, the impression formed from meeting employers' representatives, or experiences through the recruitment and selection process. Finalists also considered the level of vacancies that organisations were recruiting for as an indicator of possible employment prospects, or were influenced by employers' profile at their university.

Many final year students, however, used the 'employment proposition' as their main guide – the quality of graduate training and development an employer offers, the salary & remuneration package available, and the practical aspects of a first job, such as location or working hours.

Irrespective of the criteria that students used to arrive at their answer, the hardest part for many was just selecting a single organisation. To some extent, choosing two or three, or even half a dozen employers would have been much easier. But the whole purpose of the exercise was to replicate the reality that everyone faces – you can only work for one organisation. And at each stage of the graduate job search there are choices to be made as to which direction to take and which employers to pursue.

The resulting *Top 100* is a dynamic league table of the UK's most exciting and well-respected graduate recruiters in 2012. For a remarkable ninth consecutive year, the accounting and professional services firm PwC has been voted the UK's leading graduate employer with a total of 7.2 per cent of finalists' votes. The firm has a lead of more than four hundred votes over rivals Deloitte, who remain in second place for the seventh year running.

KPMG, another of the 'Big Four' accountancy firms, is again in third place but the widely-acclaimed Teach First scheme has seen its votes increase by almost a third this year, taking it to fourth place in the *Top 100*, its highest-ever ranking. Retailer Aldi and the NHS have each slipped down one position, to fifth and sixth places, whilst the Civil Service has moved back up one place. Ernst & Young is the only leading accountancy firm to have increased its share of the

vote this year and has climbed to eighth place, its best ranking so far. By contrast, support for the BBC has dropped by more than a third, taking it down to ninth place. After doubling its vote in the *Top 100* in 2011, the John Lewis Partnership has continued its rise up the rankings and this year is within the top ten for the first time.

Management consulting and technology firm Accenture has slipped to eleventh place, but both Tesco and Google have achieved their highest *Top 100* positions to date. Unilever has moved up the rankings for the fourth year running to reach its best ranking since 2005 and J.P. Morgan returns to the top twenty for the first time in six years. Votes for the Royal Bank of Scotland Group, however, fell by more than a quarter, taking the bank back down the rankings to 22nd place.

The highest climbers in this year's *Top 100* are led by Nestlé, which has jumped forty-four places to 47th place. Jaguar Land Rover has climbed a further thirty-four places to reach 26th place, a very impressive achievement having only rejoined in the Top 100 in 87th place two years ago. Banking group Santander has climbed twenty-seven places and last year's highest new entry Apple has now joined the top thirty, having moved up twenty-six positions. But one of last year's highest climbers has fared less well – Centrica has dropped back to 69th place – and there have been big falls too for ExxonMobil and Cancer Research UK.

There have been mixed fortunes for the leading City banking and financial institutions this year – six of the fourteen banks featured within the new *Top 100* have improved their ratings but UBS, the Lloyds Banking Group and Goldman Sachs are among those that have slipped down the rankings.

Once again, all three sections of the Armed Forces have struggled in this year's *Top 100* – the Army has slipped back in the rankings for the third year running, the Royal Navy has dropped a further seven places and the RAF has slumped to 93rd place, its lowest-ever position in the league table of leading employers. Other parts of the public sector fared little better – Local Government, the Foreign & Commonwealth Office, the Police and Transport for London all moved down the rankings for the second year running.

There are a total of nine new entries or re-entries in this year's *Top 100*, the highest being the European Commission and British Airways which return to the rankings in 56th and 78th places.

There are new entries for professional services firm Towers Watson, British Sugar and the Department for International Development – which appear in 80th, 92nd and 99th places respectively. Accounting firm BDO, Norton Rose, the Lloyd's insurance market and international conglomerate GE have each reappeared in the *Top 100*, after dropping out of the list in previous years.

Organisations leaving the *Top 100* in 2012 include Balfour Beatty, AstraZeneca, Baker & McKenzie, Sony, the Ministry of Defence, npower and three graduate employers that were re-entries in last year's rankings – the Bank of England, Simmons & Simmons and the Defence Science & Technology Laboratory (Dstl).

This year's edition of *The Times Top 100 Graduate Employers* has produced a number of significant changes within the rankings and the results provide a unique insight into how graduates from the 'Class of 2012' rated the UK's leading employers. Almost all of these organisations are featured in the 'Employer Entry' section of this book – from page 55 onwards, you can see a two-page profile for each employer, listed alphabetically for easy reference.

The editorial part of the entry includes a short description of what the organisation does, its opportunities for graduates and its recruitment programme for 2012-2013. A fact file for each employer gives details of the business functions that graduates are recruited for, the number of graduate vacancies on offer, likely starting salaries for 2013, their minimum academic requirements, application deadlines, the universities that the employer is intending to visit during the year, plus details of their graduate recruitment website and how to follow the employer on Facebook, Twitter and LinkedIn. The right-hand page of each employer entry contains a display advert promoting the organisation.

If you would like to find out more about any of the employers featured in *The Times Top 100 Graduate Employers*, then simply register with **www.Top100GraduateEmployers.com** – the official website showcasing the latest news and information about *Top 100* organisations.

Registration is entirely free and as well as being able to access the website, you'll receive regular email updates about the employers you are most interested in – this includes details of the careers events they're holding at your university during the year, up-and-coming job application deadlines, and the very latest business news about the organisations.

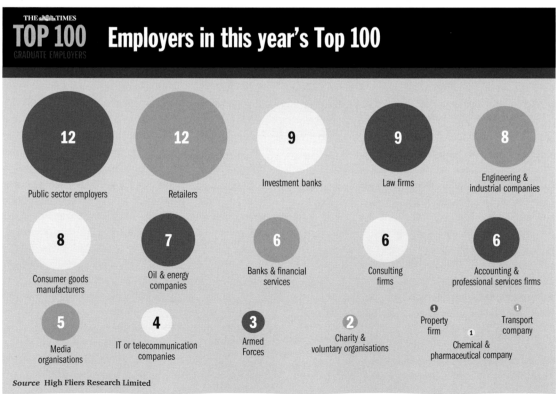

THE TIMES
TOP 100 **Employers in this year's Top 100**
GRADUATE EMPLOYERS

12	12	9	9	8
Public sector employers	Retailers	Investment banks	Law firms	Engineering & industrial companies

8	7	6	6	6
Consumer goods manufacturers	Oil & energy companies	Banks & financial services	Consulting firms	Accounting & professional services firms

5	4	3	2	1	1	1
Media organisations	IT or telecommunication companies	Armed Forces	Charity & voluntary organisations	Property firm	Chemical & pharmaceutical company	Transport company

Source High Fliers Research Limited

Talking strategy and tactics stays with you

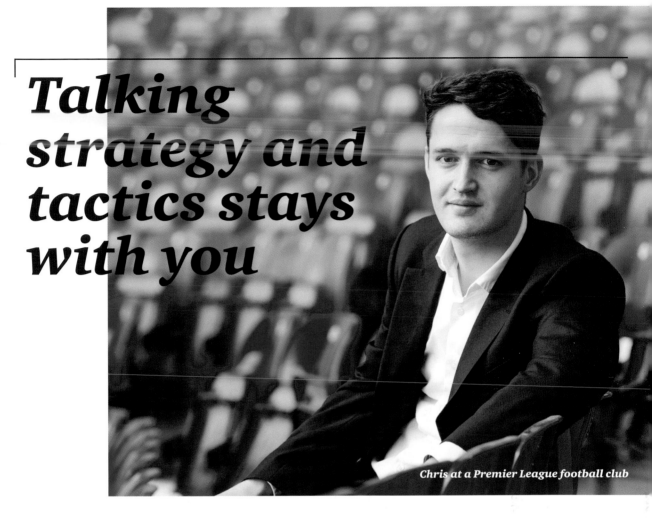

Chris at a Premier League football club

Assurance
Actuarial
Consulting
Financial Advisory
Tax
Technology

All degree disciplines,
2:1 or above.
300+ UCAS tariff
or equivalent.

Voted employer of choice by students in The Times Top 100 Graduate Employers Survey for nine years running.

Opportunities with the UK's number one graduate employer

Offices across the UK » Join Spring, Summer or Autumn

Your career is just that, yours. You choose it. You live it. You make it happen. To get the best from it, you need the best opportunities. That's why opportunities are at the heart of a career with us. Opportunities to grow as an individual, to build lasting relationships and make an impact in a place where people, quality and value mean everything. For Chris, this means working with a Premier League football club. As an Assurance Associate, his job is to look beyond the cost of a new player, or the price of a replica kit, and understand what makes their business tick. Join PwC – we're focused on helping you reach your full potential.

It's the opportunity of a lifetime.

www.pwc.com/uk/careers

www.facebook.com/PwCCareersUK

pwc

Diverse people make us stronger

Anything but ordinary.

Few jobs for inexperienced graduates

Poor job prospects for 2012 graduates

○ A third of graduate jobs will be taken by those who finished cour... in 2010 or earlier...

substantially expanding their intake. But despite the increase, the report, compiled b... liers Rese...

Students 'in early jobs search'

Students are appl...ng for more j... at an earlier...

...f those without work experi-

...year the UK G...te Careers ...nt in the job ...become less ...years or go ...the study by

Graduates putting their careers first

CHRIS MARSHALL

MORE and more graduates are

...r stud...ir 2009-10 and...

More jobs for this year's graduates

Students start the search early for jobs

More than two-fifths of students applied for jobs almost a year before leaving university.

A stud... ...final year

Survey 2012 found.
To avoid disappointment in the job market, graduates have become less inclined to take... year...

how hard today's university students are working to get a graduate job at the end... their degr...

to work in inner-city schools. It will be the third biggest recruiter of graduates this year behind PwC and Deloitte. The Civil Service fast track career progress scheme is ...p increasing its recruitment.

...ut High Flier Research, which ...piled the analysis w...

Tough outlook for class of 2012 as third of jobs go to recent graduates

Graduate employment shows encouraging signs

At the top of the graduate labour market the average ...

remaining constant."
But polling by High Fli-...w Res...ch of ...100 top ...elect-...versity ...worse ...arting ...ted to ...the ...at a ...

Top employers look to take on more graduates

BRITAIN'S leading employers are expecting to increase their graduate recruitment by 6.4 per cent in 2012 – three times the rise a year earlier, research shows.

The same survey – The Graduate Market in 2012 – also discovered more than half of the 100 employers interviewed plan to recruit more graduates in 2012 th...

past few weeks we've had playground designers, schools, broadcasting system companies, festival organisers, communication agencies and fashion forecasters addin... new roles.

"That's just the tip of the iceberg, reall... We also know Southampton Solent studen... who only finished their studies this mon... h...ve already been...epted into gradua... ...such as Mans... ...rvices and Cap...

Backlog of graduates creates 'job bottleneck'

...rs are ...ke by ...year ...First, ...heme ...ini...

More jobs on offer for 2012 graduates

...univ...ty "class of 2012" could ...

...the overall job mar... ...tes know they need... ...s seriously. ...e Careers Survey 2... ...r students gradua... ...dy applied for jo... ...er 2011, just as ...of study. ...ng more compet...

GRADUATES are comp... ...r top jobs against a bac... ...f university leavers strugg... ...find work, a report wa... ...day.
One in three applications for ...r's graduate vacancies are fr... ...dents who left higher edu... ...last year or earlier. ...d almost half of applicants f... ...il and public sector roles a... ...graduates according to th... ...ual study from High Fliers ...ket research a...

More than 50 graduate... chase every vacancy with top UK firms

CHRIS MARSHALL
...ESPONDENT

Martin Birchall, the managing director of High Fliers Re-...

...ployers received 52 applicatio... for each graduate job in 20... compared with 47 in 2011...

Understanding the Graduate Job Market

By **Martin Birchall**
Managing Director, High Fliers Research

Whether it was the continuing Euro crisis, the UK slipping back into recession or record levels of youth unemployment, anyone graduating from university in the summer of 2012 will have seen a relentless barrage of discouraging newspaper headlines while they were trying to find their first graduate job.

And much of the attention on the graduate employment market focused on the continuing stiff competition for entry-level jobs, the glut of graduates from previous years who failed to find work after their degrees, and the limited prospects for new graduates without previous work experience.

There was rather less coverage of the positive news that Britain's top employers increased their graduate vacancies again in 2012, the third year running that opportunities for university-leavers at *The Times Top 100 Graduate Employers* have risen.

And the outlook for the 'Class of 2013' seems encouraging too – the latest analysis shows that graduate vacancies at the leading employers are set to increase by a further 7.2 per cent in 2013. Nearly half of the organisations in the *Top 100* plan to hire more graduates this year than they did in 2012, two-fifths believe they will recruit similar numbers, while a sixth expect to reduce their graduate intake. Together, the employers in this year's *Top 100* are advertising a total of 18,306 jobs, compared to the 17,084 graduates hired in 2012.

This year graduate recruitment will again be dominated by the country's largest accountancy & professional services firms who expect to increase their trainee places by at least 10 per cent, compared with the number of graduates hired in 2012. The 'Big Four' accounting firms – Deloitte, Ernst & Young, KPMG and PwC – plan to recruit 4,100 trainees in 2013.

> **❝** *Graduate recruitment will again be dominated by the country's largest accounting & professional services firms.* **❞**

Although the banking sector was one of the employment areas hardest hit at the start of the recession in 2008, the City's top investment banks have stepped up their graduate intake twice during the last three years and are set to expand their vacancies by nearly 11 per cent during 2012-2013.

Employers in a total of thirteen of the seventeen industries and business sectors represented within *The Times Top 100 Graduate Employers* are optimistic about graduate recruitment in 2013. The UK's leading consumer goods manufacturers are planning to recruit up to a fifth more graduates in the coming year and there are welcome increases in vacancies too at consulting firms, media organisations, banking & financial services,

Nestlé
Good Food, Good Life

Nestlé | **ACADEMY**
Unlocking your potential

I want to create a
better world
and build a better
business

At Nestlé, we encourage our people to grow in more than one dimension, to achieve all they can be both professionally and personally.

Joining Nestlé means you'll be joining a business which combines the freedom to implement locally relevant plans, with the opportunity to call on the global expertise of the world's leading nutrition, health and wellness company. We look to enhance the quality of life everywhere, every day.... creating long-term sustainable value for our consumers, for our communities, and for our shareholders.

At Nestlé there are no limits to your success, if you want it we'll help you get it!
Our Academy offers you a lifetime of learning throughout your career offering development and support every step of the way to make sure that you achieve both professional and personal career fulfilment.

The start of your Nestlé Academy journey could be one of our
Graduate Programmes in the following areas:
CPUK (Cereal Partners UK) • Engineering • Finance • HR • Manufacturing & Focused Improvement
Marketing • Quality Assurance • Sales • SHE (Safety, Health & Environment) • Supply Chain
We also offer 12 month placement opportunities as well as Summer Internships.

Find out more about what is out there for you at: http://www.nestlecareers.co.uk

oil & energy companies, IT & telecommunications companies, law firms and retailers.

In the engineering & industrial, transport and charity sectors, vacancy numbers are unchanged but there are likely to be slightly fewer graduate opportunities at chemical & pharmaceuticals companies and in the Armed Forces in the year ahead.

There are now an average of 185 vacancies per *Top 100* employer but a quarter of organisations plan to hire more than 250 new recruits and three employers anticipate hiring at least 1,000 university-leavers in 2013. The largest number of vacancies are at the accounting & professional services firms (25.1 per cent of total graduate jobs) and investment banks (13.1 per cent of total).

Despite recruitment freezes elsewhere in the public sector, the thirteen Government departments and agencies appearing in the latest *Top 100* rankings actually increased their graduate recruitment by almost a fifth in 2012 and are planning to maintain their graduate intake for 2013 at similar levels.

The huge expansion of the Teach First scheme over the last three years means that it is expected to be the biggest individual employer of graduates in *The Times Top 100 Graduate Employers* in 2013, with 1,260 places available. Other major recruiters include PwC and Deloitte (1,200 vacancies each), KPMG (900 vacancies) and Ernst & Young (800 vacancies). And leading engine manufacturer Rolls-Royce is set to almost double its annual graduate intake to 400 vacancies for the first time.

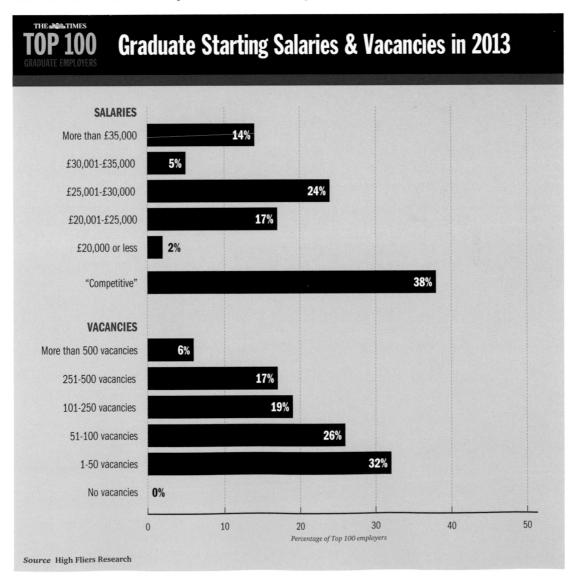

THE TIMES
TOP 100 **Graduate Starting Salaries & Vacancies in 2013**
GRADUATE EMPLOYERS

SALARIES

More than £35,000	14%
£30,001-£35,000	5%
£25,001-£30,000	24%
£20,001-£25,000	17%
£20,000 or less	2%
"Competitive"	38%

VACANCIES

More than 500 vacancies	6%
251-500 vacancies	17%
101-250 vacancies	19%
51-100 vacancies	26%
1-50 vacancies	32%
No vacancies	0%

Percentage of Top 100 employers

Source High Fliers Research

Three-fifths of the employers featured in this year's *Top 100* have vacancies for graduates in financial management, at least half have opportunities in IT, more than two-fifths are recruiting for human resources, around a third are hiring engineering or general management graduates, over a quarter are looking for recruits to work in marketing, whilst a fifth want retail personnel, sales executives or have roles in research & development.

More than four-fifths of *Top 100* employers have graduate vacancies in London and half have posts available elsewhere in the south east of England. At least half also have vacancies in the north west and south west of England, the Midlands and in Yorkshire. East Anglia, Wales and Northern Ireland have the fewest graduate vacancies.

Graduate starting salaries at Britain's leading employers have increased in eight of the last ten years – including two significant rises during the recession – but more than three-quarters of the organisations featured in this year's edition of *The Times Top 100 Graduate Employers* have opted to leave their starting salaries unchanged from 2012 rates. Fewer than a fifth of employers have announced increases to their graduate packages for 2013, generally by five per cent or less. The average salary for graduates in 2012 was £29,000.

Two-fifths of *Top 100* employers simply describe their salary packages for next year as "competitive". A fifth expect to offer new graduates up to £25,000 and fourteen organisations – mainly City law firms, investment banks or the leading oil & energy companies – are planning to pay starting salaries in excess of £35,000. The most generous graduate package publicised within this edition of the *Top 100* is again for retailer Aldi – they continue to offer new recruits a market-leading starting salary of £40,000 and an Audi A4 car.

Half of the UK's leading employers now recruit graduates year-round (or in different phases during the year) and will accept applications throughout the 2012-2013 recruitment season, until all their vacancies have been filled. For employers with a single application deadline, most are in either November or December, although the leading law firms usually have July closing dates.

Seven out of ten employers now insist that applicants for their graduate programmes should have a 2.1 degree or better and a quarter specify a minimum UCAS tariff, typically in the range of 240 to 320 – the equivalent of 'CCC' to 'ABB' at A-level.

So for those who make the grade, there continue to be an excellent range of career opportunities and some great starting salaries on offer from *The Times Top 100 Graduate Employers* in 2013.

THE TIMES TOP 100 GRADUATE EMPLOYERS — Graduate Vacancies at Top 100 Employers in 2013

	2012		NUMBER OF VACANCIES	% OF TOTAL VACANCIES	CHANGE SINCE 2012
1.	1	ACCOUNTANCY & PROFESSIONAL SERVICES FIRMS	4,600	25.1	▲ 10.0%
2.	2	INVESTMENT BANKS	2,400	13.1	▲ 10.7%
3.	3	PUBLIC SECTOR EMPLOYERS	2,305	12.6	▲ 0.8%
4.	6	ENGINEERING & INDUSTRIAL COMPANIES	1,510	8.2	NO CHANGE
5.	5	BANKING & FINANCIAL SERVICES	1,397	7.6	▲ 13.6%
6.	4	RETAILERS	1,375	7.5	▲ 5.3%
7.	7	ARMED FORCES	830	4.5	▼ 5.9%
8.	8	LAW FIRMS	795	4.3	▲ 6.0%
9.	11	IT & TELECOMMUNICATION COMPANIES	695	3.8	▲ 6.1%
10.	9	CONSULTING FIRMS	675	3.7	▲ 17.4%
11.	10	OIL & ENERGY COMPANIES	640	3.5	▲ 8.5%
12.	13	MEDIA ORGANISATIONS	455	2.5	▲ 15.8%
13.	12	CONSUMER GOODS MANUFACTURERS	359	2.0	▲ 17.7%
14.	14	CHARITY OR VOLUNTARY ORGANISATIONS	100	0.5	NO CHANGE
15.	-	TRANSPORT COMPANIES	70	0.4	NO CHANGE
16.	15	CHEMICAL & PHARMACEUTICAL COMPANIES	50	0.3	▼ 3.8%
17.	16	PROPERTY FIRMS	50	0.3	▲ 4.2%

Source High Fliers Research

DID YOU
THINK
WE WERE
JUST
ABOUT
sugar?

THINK AGAIN.

SEE FOR YOURSELF ON PAGE 96 >

WWW.NOTJUSTSUGAR.COM

Our ideas don't just take off, they're out of this world.

Blue sky thinking. Why stop there? At Mars we like to boldly go... Well you know how the rest of it goes. And launching M&Ms into space as the official snack of the space shuttle is right up there when it comes to an example of what we mean. You see, we offer our associates the opportunity to think and operate in innovative ways, across all of our billion-dollar brands. Which means you won't just have the freedom to shape our privately-owned business. You'll have the freedom to develop and grow as an individual. Think of it as infinite space. But the final frontier? Well, that's up to you. Check out what we mean on page 168 or click **mars.co.uk/graduates**

MAKE IT MEAN MORE | **MARS**

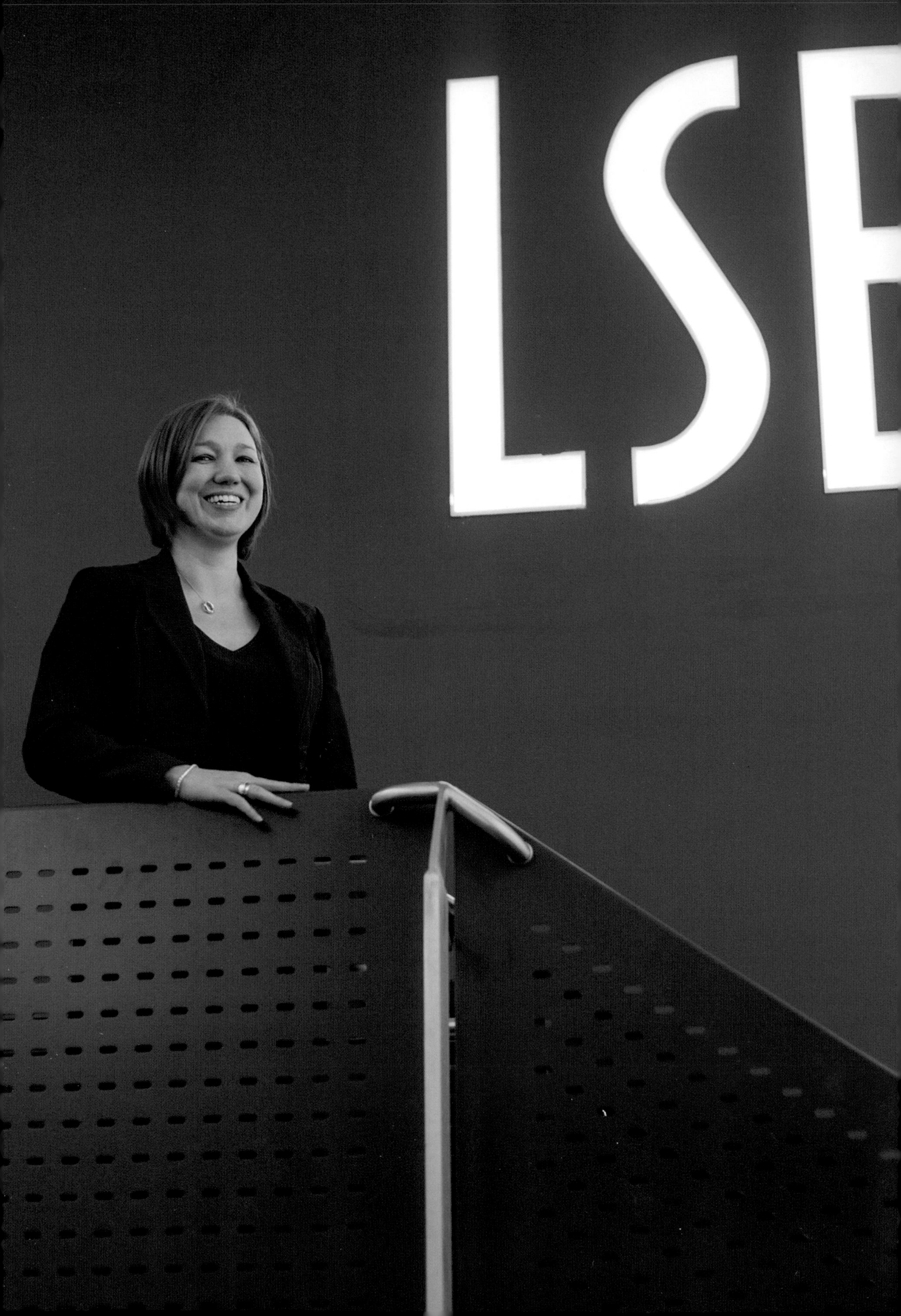
LSE

Successful Job Hunting

By **Jenny Owen**
Director, LSE Careers Service, London School of Economics

You'll never have more opportunities offered to you on a plate than when you walk through the doors of university. The challenge is how can you wring the experience for everything that it's got to offer, so that when you start preparing for life after university and planning what you'd like to do for your career, you have a better understanding of yourself and what makes you 'tick'.

Throw yourself into your studies whole heartedly – you only get one shot at your degree – but get involved in as many clubs and societies as you can too, whether you're already thinking about work and job opportunities or not. The more extra-curricular things you do, the sooner you'll begin to get a feel for 'do I really enjoy this or enjoy that' and the sort of skills and strengths you could offer a future employer.

It's also worth getting in touch with your university careers service as early as you can. Increasing numbers of students are now doing this in their first year, so that they can find out about internships or work placement opportunities, or are taking advantage of the fact that there may be less academic pressure earlier in their degree courses to spend time researching their career options. Internships are certainly becoming increasingly important to employers and in sectors like investment banking, up to three-quarters of graduate jobs are being offered to students who've done an internship with the bank during their studies, usually at the end of their second year.

For many people, their first experience of their careers service may be through its website. Every careers service in the country has its own website and many include useful tools that can help you decide which career areas may be right for you, as well as destination data that shows what graduates from different courses have gone on to do after university, and details of employers who are actively targeting your university for their graduate recruitment. Careers services have worked very hard to present a wealth of useful careers content and information from the outside world in a way that is most suitable for your particular university. This means someone has already done the hard work and filtered it to make it as relevant to you as possible.

Don't be afraid of going along to your university careers service in person, especially if you're one of the thousands of students each year who has little or no idea what they want to do after university. Careers services are really good at helping you to understand the experiences that you've had and then matching them with potential careers

❝ It may seem such a cliché, but five well-crafted applications will always be better than fifty rushed ones. ❞

See more. Be more.

Future Leaders Development Programme

Barclays Retail and Business Banking offers you the chance to become a leader in a global financial services organisation that serves 48 million customers in over 50 countries. Over the course of the programme, you'll gain an amazing perspective on the world of banking and an exceptional insight into business leadership.

Now turn to page 80 to see and learn more.

seemore-bemore.com/TT100

Talk and follow us at

t @barclaysgrads   **f** Barclays Graduates

Retail and Business Banking

BARCLAYS

and types of work. Because careers advisers are entirely independent, they don't have a vested interest in you or preconceived ideas about what you 'should' do. Many students get their ideas about careers from their parents, their friends or their tutors – people to whom it matters a great deal what happens to them – whereas careers advisers just want you to make the right decision for you.

At many universities you can see careers advisers on a one-to-one basis for an in-depth consultation, but this usually requires booking in advance, especially at the busiest times of year. Otherwise advisers will be available on a drop-in basis for quick queries or shorter discussions, or through group sessions.

The term 'careers adviser' can be a bit of a misnomer, in that whilst most advisers will provide advice and coaching about the job hunting process and the practicalities of preparing applications to employers, the other part of their role – helping students determine their career choice – is much more consultative. It would be great if a careers adviser could take one look at you and say 'congratulations, you're going to be a policy adviser' and send you off to do it, but that's not how things work. The guidance and direction that careers advisers can provide comes through talking through what you've done, the things you enjoy and what you might want to do in the future. You can't turn up and say 'I don't know what I want to do' and then just sit there and wait for someone to tell you.

It can often be about broadening horizons – people often come to university with a very narrow idea of the range of careers that are available to them, such as being a doctor, dentist, teacher or accountant. So the first thing that an adviser might do would be to explain how to investigate what else is out there and then help you narrow those options back down to a few areas that you feel the greatest connection to.

One thing a careers adviser won't do is tell you which individual employers are the best in a particular sector. The 'best' is a highly subjective term and an organisation that is a good choice for you may not be right for the person you sit next to in lectures.

There are plenty of practical things you can do to find out about the culture and opportunities available from different employers. Start by using your existing networks – think about the people you know and those that they know to find out whether there is somebody already working in the kind of fields that you're interested in. Networking is a key skill for getting on in the world of work and people are often very happy to talk about their own experiences and the organisations they're working for. And don't forget, most careers services have an extensive alumni database available to help current students make contact with graduates in a wide variety of career areas.

Many university careers services run a programme of events to help students understand particular industries, job types or business sectors, which can also be a great opportunity for informal networking and discussion with recent graduates.

Careers fairs that are held at universities across the country are a good way to discover which organisations are recruiting and can be a great opportunity to meet with employers in person, particularly if you're getting close to deciding which companies to apply to.

It's all too easy to be overwhelmed by careers fairs, especially at the larger events so you should definitely check out which employers are going to the fair in advance and have a plan of action in mind. Don't just do a circuit through the middle of the hall grabbing a few freebies en-route and exit without actually having a conversation – simply arriving through the doors and then leaving again doesn't mean you've done anything about your career.

Pick off the companies that most interest you and think 'right, by the time I exit this event I want these questions answered and I want to have spoken to these recruiters'. It's also important that you do your homework beforehand and look at employers' websites and brochures so that you've understood the basics about the organisations you're going to meet. Wandering up to the HM Revenue and Customs stand and asking 'So what do you do?' isn't likely to make the best impression.

If you know that you're particularly keen on working for an individual employer then it's worth seeing if they're holding a presentation or other event at your university. Many employers offer skills sessions, where their recruiters or managers talk about a generic skill such as leadership or run a workshop about their business area or industry. This can be a really nice way to start to develop a skill that you might need to show when you apply for graduate jobs, as well as being a chance to 'test the water' for what working in a particular career area might be like.

Employers also offer more conventional campus recruitment events, although many are moving away from the 'death by Powerpoint' approach in favour of less formal networking sessions with recent graduates, recruiters and line managers or run workshops which advise on how to make a successful job application. Again, it's important that you prepare beforehand and make sure you don't simply ask questions that are answered on the company's graduate recruitment website.

When it comes to making applications – either for internships or a full-time graduate job – the key to being successful is careful preparation. Start by keeping a diary and jot down everything you've done at university. With so many students applying to employers, what really helps make an application seem convincing is facts and figures, so try and include as many dates, times, places and details of all the things you've taken part in. If you were involved in running an amazing RAG team or organised a great society social, note down how many people were involved and what you achieved, rather than just saying 'I worked in a team'.

Even though the majority of the larger and best-known employers will insist that you complete their own online application form, it's still well worth compiling a CV. It's a great way of bringing together all the key information that you'll need in one place and will help you organise how you're going to present yourself to employers.

When it comes to filling in an individual employer's application, start by simply bullet pointing the examples that you want to use for each question. That way you can check you're using the best possible examples for each part of the application – it's all too easy to provide an example of leadership when you're being asked about teamwork and then over the page write all about teamwork in response to a leadership question. Just like an essay or dissertation, you need to have a definite plan and structure in place first, before you spend ages crafting beautiful prose.

It may seem such a cliché but five well-crafted applications will always be better than fifty rushed ones. Recruiters can spot a generic, cut and pasted application a mile off and it won't impress them. The scattergun approach to applications rarely

works, because it's very difficult to convey any kind of real enthusiasm for a particular role or an organisation if everything else on your application form is the same as all the others you've made.

If your initial application is successful then you may well be asked to do online tests and a pre-screening telephone interview, before you get to the first main interview round of the selection process. Your careers service will be able to help you prepare for these tests, either through the resources on their website, practice material at the careers service or through group training sessions, where you can talk through the techniques needed for different tests such as numeracy or verbal reasoning.

When it comes to preparing for interview, the first step is to remind yourself what information your interviewer will have in front of them. Always keep a copy of your applications and re-read them thoroughly before your interview. Many interviewers are still using competency-based interviewing techniques and you can take a good guess at what they'll ask at interview from what they asked on the original application form. For example, you may have described one instance of teamwork on your application, so it would be good to prepare a second that's a different story.

But there's also a real trend emerging for graduate recruiters to use strength-based interviews. The people who do well at these are those that understand themselves and what makes them tick – this means all the preparatory work that you did in terms of working out where you want to be and what you might be is doubly useful. If you are particularly concerned about the type of questions you may face, then check with your careers service – they will be able to provide sample questions and there are recruitment websites which include tips for common questions at individual employers' interviews. Most services are also able to offer mock interviews, which can be really helpful to get some immediate feedback on your interview technique.

The final selection round for most major employers is likely to be some kind of assessment centre. The format of these varies but they often include group exercises, some kind of workplace simulation such as in-box exercise or problem-solving case study and, of course, more interviews. You're also likely to be re-tested for the tests that you completed online, just to make sure that you

The Actuarial Profession
making financial sense of the future

Actuaries can't predict the **future** ... but we can predict its **impact**

Actuaries can calculate the probability of future events occurring and quantify those risks to a business.

They are problem solvers and strategic thinkers with a deep understanding of financial systems. They work in a variety of exciting roles internationally. An actuarial career is one of the most diverse and rewarding in the world.

Where could you work?

Every area of business is subject to risks so an actuarial career offers many options. A typical business problem might involve analysing future financial events, especially when the amount or timing of a payment is uncertain. It could also involve assessing when and where devastating storms may hit to help predict risks, and their associated costs, for investments or insurance.

Salaries for graduate trainee actuaries are around £25,000-£30,000 and as you become more senior this can rise to well over £150,000. So the rewards are substantial.

How do I find out more?

To find out how to become an actuary, the benefits of studying towards an actuarial qualification and areas that actuaries work in, then look at the following web link www.actuaries.org.uk/becoming-actuary/pages/how-become-actuary or contact our careers team.

Email: careers@actuaries.org.uk
Telephone: 01865 268 228

www.**actuaries**.org.uk

didn't get your friends to do the answers for you. Again, there is plenty of help available from your careers services to practice the different types of exercises that you may encounter.

On the day, take confidence from the fact that only a very small proportion of those who applied initially get through to this final round, so the odds of being successful are very good at this stage – no recruiter is going to interview somebody who they don't think stands a good chance of getting the job. Be aware too that through the assessment centre, different people will be assessing different elements, so if the group discussion goes horribly wrong for you, there's plenty of chances to make up for it in the other sessions.

Once the assessment centres are over, if you're in the happy position of having more than one job offer, how should you make the final decision about which employer to join? For most students, their gut feel about which offer to accept is often a strong one – whether it's a preference for a particular brand, a better feeling about the people they've met during the recruitment process or simply that one job offer is for the part of the country that they most want to work in. What is a real mistake is to be influenced by where your parents think you should go or where your friends have had offers from.

In the end, you should think about which organisation makes you feel 'yes, this is somewhere I can build a career'.

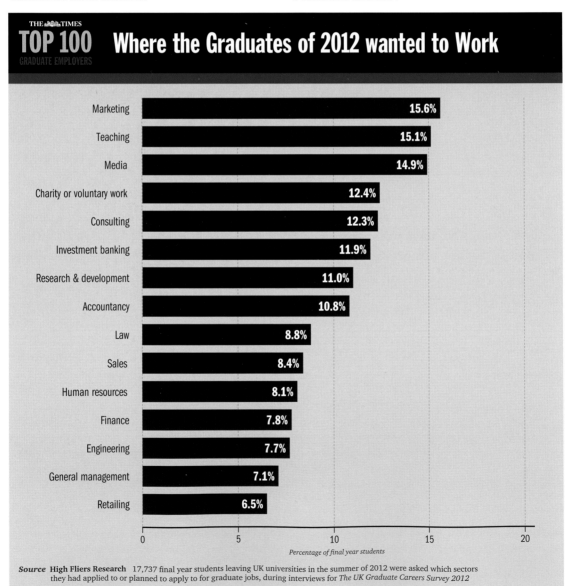

THE TIMES
TOP 100 Where the Graduates of 2012 wanted to Work
GRADUATE EMPLOYERS

- Marketing — 15.6%
- Teaching — 15.1%
- Media — 14.9%
- Charity or voluntary work — 12.4%
- Consulting — 12.3%
- Investment banking — 11.9%
- Research & development — 11.0%
- Accountancy — 10.8%
- Law — 8.8%
- Sales — 8.4%
- Human resources — 8.1%
- Finance — 7.8%
- Engineering — 7.7%
- General management — 7.1%
- Retailing — 6.5%

Percentage of final year students

Source **High Fliers Research** 17,737 final year students leaving UK universities in the summer of 2012 were asked which sectors they had applied to or planned to apply to for graduate jobs, during interviews for *The UK Graduate Careers Survey 2012*

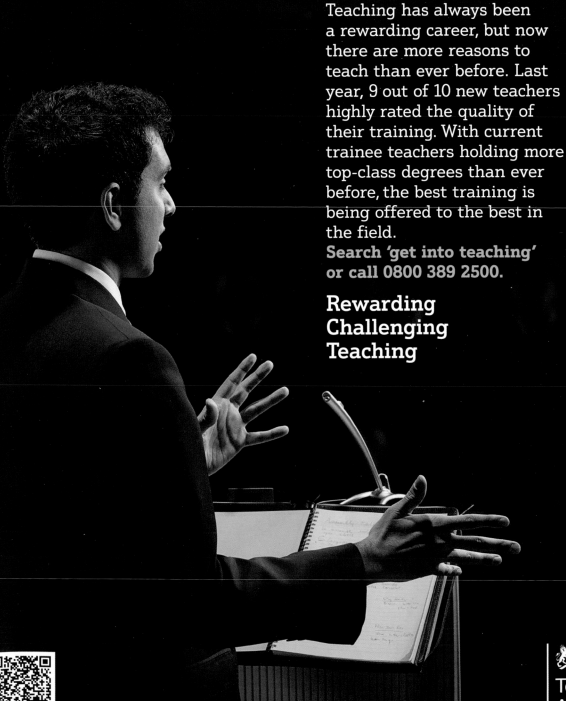

Give motivational team talks to hundreds of people.

Every Friday in assembly.

Teaching has always been a rewarding career, but now there are more reasons to teach than ever before. Last year, 9 out of 10 new teachers highly rated the quality of their training. With current trainee teachers holding more top-class degrees than ever before, the best training is being offered to the best in the field.

Search 'get into teaching' or call 0800 389 2500.

**Rewarding
Challenging
Teaching**

Teaching
Agency

TOP 100 GRADUATE EMPLOYERS 1999-2000

TOP 100 GRADUATE EMPLOYERS 2005-2006

THE TIMES TOP 100 GRADUATE EMPLOYERS

THE TIMES GRADUATE EMPLOYERS 2004-2005

THE TIMES TOP 100 GRADUATE

THE TIMES TOP 100 GRADUATE EMPLOYERS

THE TIMES TOP 100 GRADUATE EMPLOYERS

THE TIMES GRADUATE EMPLOYERS 2001-2002

TIMES TOP 100 GRADUATE EMPLOYERS

TIMES TOP 100 GRADUATE EMPLOYERS 2003-2004

TOP 100 GRADUATE EMPLOYERS 2007-2008

THE TIMES

TOP 100 GRADUATE EMPLOYERS 2010-2011

Fifteen Years of Researching Britain's Top Employers

By **Gill Thomas**
Publisher, *The Times Top 100 Graduate Employers*

It's now fifteen years since the original edition of The Times Top 100 Graduate Employers league table was produced in 1997, revealing for the first time which organisations the UK's top undergraduates aspired to work for after their studies.

It turned out to be quite a year – Tony Blair and New Labour swept into Government, ending eighteen years of Conservative rule, the UK won the Eurovision Song Contest and Hong Kong was returned to China. Bill Clinton began his second term as President of the United States, Diana Princess of Wales was killed in a car crash in Paris, and a previously-unknown web domain 'Google' was registered in California.

For new graduates fresh out of university, 1997 was a great time to be job hunting. In just twelve months, vacancies had risen by nearly a fifth, the largest increase in graduate jobs since the late 1980s, and salaries continued to rise well above the rate of inflation. Final year students participating in *The UK Graduate Careers Survey 1997* – the annual survey of finalists' career aspirations and expectations that is used to compile *The Times Top 100 Graduate Employers* – voted Marks & Spencer the year's top graduate employer and more finalists applied for jobs in engineering than any other area.

It is interesting to compare the results of that survey with the similar research carried out with the 'Class of 2012' earlier this year. Fifteen years ago, six of the top ten employers that students thought offered the best opportunities for graduates were manufacturing or industrial companies. By contrast, none of the organisations in this year's top ten actually make anything – the list is dominated instead by accounting & professional services firms and public sector employers.

> **"** *Only four organisations have made it to number one since The Times Top 100 Graduate Employers began in 1997.* **"**

This year, typical salaries at a *Top 100* graduate employer are £29,000, an impressive 87% higher than the starting rates for graduates in 1997. The average then was £15,500 and fewer than thirty employers offered new recruits packages of £20,000 or more.

Fifteen years ago, fewer than one in eight finalists used the internet to research their career options but record numbers supported local university careers fairs. During the 2011-2012 recruitment season, although virtually every graduate job hunter relied on employers' websites as a key source of graduate job information, attendances at campus events such as recruitment presentations and skills training workshops remain as strong as ever.

Only four organisations have made it to number one since *The Times Top 100 Graduate Employers*

YOU'RE THE DIFFERENCE
BETWEEN A SUMMER SKILL
AND A REWARDING FUTURE

Now I've got a taste for working inside one of the UK's top financial companies – I know I'll be back for more.

Internship Opportunities

Sarah was surprised to learn that a 10-week internship could give her a taste for much bigger things – like a more rewarding career at Lloyds Banking Group. She's already had the opportunity to interview our top senior leaders for an intranet story and now we've invited her to interview for our HR Graduate Programme. So Sarah can look forward to a more exciting future. Like her, you too could open new doors with Lloyds Banking Group. Because, when it comes to making us the UK's Best Bank for Customers – we know you can be the difference.

lloydsbankinggrouptalent.com

LLOYDS BANKING GROUP

 Lloyds TSB   HALIFAX   ❋ BANK OF SCOTLAND

began in 1997. Accenture (originally known as Andersen Consulting, the consulting arm of accounting firm Arthur Andersen) stormed to the top spot in 1998 and remained there for five years. Their reign heralded a huge surge in popularity for careers in consulting and at its peak in 2001, almost one in six university graduates applied for jobs in the sector. In the year before the firm changed its name, Andersen Consulting astutely introduced a new graduate package that included a £28,500 starting salary (a sky-high figure for graduates in 2000) and a much talked-about £10,000 bonus, helping to assure the firm's popularity, irrespective of its corporate branding.

In 2003, after two dismal years in graduate recruitment when vacancies for university-leavers dropped by more than a fifth following the terrorist attacks of 11th September 2001, the Civil Service was named Britain's leading graduate employer. A year later it was displaced by PricewaterhouseCoopers, the accounting and professional services firm formed from the merger of Price Waterhouse and Coopers & Lybrand in 1998. At the time, the firm was the largest private-sector recruiter of graduates, with an intake in 2004 of more than a thousand trainees.

PricewaterhouseCoopers (now known simply as PwC) has remained at number one for a unprecedented nine years running, increasing its share of the student vote from five per cent in 2004 to more than 10 per cent in 2007. The following year, the firm faced its stiffest competition yet from

rivals Deloitte and retained the top ranking by just seven votes, but the margin between the firms has increased again since and this year more than four hundred votes separated the two employers.

PwC's reign as the leading employer represents a real renaissance for the entire accounting sector. Whereas fifteen years ago, a career in accountancy was widely regarded as a safe, traditional employment choice and the firms themselves were often derided as being 'dull', 'boring' or just 'bean-counters', today's profession is viewed in a very different light. The training required to become a chartered accountant is now seen as a prized business qualification and the sector's leading firms are regularly described as 'prestigious', 'dynamic' and 'international' by undergraduates looking for their first job after university. Accountancy's transformation is underlined by the fact that fewer than seven per cent of final year students opted for one of the top six accounting firms in the *Top 100* of 1997, compared with the 19 per cent of votes polled by the 'Big Four' firms in this year's list.

A total of 194 different organisations have now appeared within *The Times Top 100 Graduate Employers* since its inception and over seventy of these have made it into the rankings every year for the last decade. The most consistent performers since 1997 have been PwC, the Civil Service and Accenture, each of which have never been lower than 11th place in the league table. The NHS has also had a formidable record, appearing in every top ten since 2002, and the BBC, Goldman Sachs

---

THE TIMES TOP 100 GRADUATE EMPLOYERS — Movers & Shakers in the Top 100

HIGHEST NEW ENTRIES		HIGHEST CLIMBING EMPLOYERS	
1998	MICROSOFT (38th)	1998	J.P. MORGAN (UP 8 PLACES)
1999	PFIZER (31st)	1999	SCHLUMBERGER (UP 13 PLACES)
2000	MORGAN STANLEY (34th)	2000	CAPITAL ONE (UP 32 PLACES)
2001	MARCONI (36th)	2001	EUROPEAN COMMISSION (UP 36 PLACES)
2002	GUINNESS UDV (44th)	2002	WPP (UP 36 PLACES)
2003	ASDA (40th)	2003	ROLLS-ROYCE (UP 37 PLACES)
2004	BAKER & MCKENZIE (61st)	2004	J.P. MORGAN (UP 29 PLACES)
2005	PENGUIN (70th)	2005	TEACH FIRST (UP 22 PLACES)
2006	FUJITSU (81st)	2006	GOOGLE (UP 32 PLACES)
2007	BDO STOY HAYWARD (74th)	2007	PFIZER (UP 30 PLACES)
2008	SKY (76th)	2008	CO-OPERATIVE GROUP (UP 39 PLACES)
2009	BDO STOY HAYWARD (68th)	2009	CADBURY (UP 48 PLACES)
2010	SAATCHI & SAATCHI (49th)	2010	ASDA (UP 41 PLACES)
2011	APPLE (53rd)	2011	CENTRICA (UP 41 PLACES)
2012	EUROPEAN COMMISSION (56th)	2012	NESTLÉ (UP 44 PLACES)

Source High Fliers Research

If you fit in here 'You'll fit in here

Graduate opportunities
UK-based

Safeguarding the UK against threats to national security requires talented people. We recruit graduates with the potential to increase the skills within our organisation, to make it even more effective. Our staff comes from an increasingly diverse range of backgrounds and this in-depth understanding of different communities, cultures and languages is crucial for our work. What unique talents could you bring to help protect the UK?

Find out more at
www.mi5.gov.uk/careers

To apply you must be a British citizen. Discretion is vital. You should not discuss your application, other than with your partner or a close family member.

SECURITYSERVICE
MI5

and Ernst & Young have all remained within the top twenty throughout the last decade.

Google, Barclays Capital, MI5 – The Security Service, Aldi and Jaguar Land Rover have each climbed more than sixty places within the *Top 100* during the last fifteen years.

Other employers haven't been so successful. Chemical company ICI, ranked in 5th place in 1997, dropped out of the *Top 100* altogether in 2001. Ford, which was once rated as high as 14th, disappeared out of the list in 2006 after cancelling its graduate recruitment programme two years previously and BT dropped an eye-watering forty-seven places in a single year when it pulled out of its 2009-2010 university recruitment campaign.

Twenty nine employers – including the Home Office, Nokia, Coca-Cola, the Met Office, Capgemini and United Biscuits – have the dubious record

of having only been ranked in the *Top 100* once during the last fifteen years. And Marconi had the unusual distinction of being one of the highest-ever new entries in 36th place in 2001, only to vanish from the list entirely the following year.

One of the most spectacular ascendancies within the *Top 100* has been the rise and rise of Aldi which joined the list in 65th place in 2002 and rose to 3rd place in 2009, helped in part by its eye-catching remuneration package for new graduates (currently £40,000 plus an Audi A4 car).

And Teach First has been another runaway success in the rankings. After appearing as a new entry in 63rd place in 2003, the scheme rose each year until 2010. Teach First is now in 4th place and is all set to become the UK's largest graduate recruiter, with 1,260 places available on its two-year programme in 2013.

THE TIMES
TOP 100 Winners & Losers in the Top 100
GRADUATE EMPLOYERS

MOST CONSISTENT EMPLOYERS 1997-2012	HIGHEST RANKING	LOWEST RANKING
ARTHUR ANDERSEN	2nd (1998-2001)	3rd (1997, 2002)
PWC	1st (2004-2012)	3rd (1999-2001, 2003)
CIVIL SERVICE	8th (1997, 2011)	1st (2003)
ACCENTURE	1st (1998-2002)	11th (2012)
IBM	12th (1997)	25th (1998)
ERNST & YOUNG	8th (2012)	21st (1998)
GLAXOSMITHKLINE	11th (2000)	26th (1998)
KPMG	3rd (2006-2008, 2011-2012)	20th (1997)
ARMY	4th (2003)	23rd (2012)
PROCTER & GAMBLE	2nd (1997)	21st (2012)

EMPLOYERS CLIMBING HIGHEST 1997-2012	NEW ENTRY RANKING	HIGHEST RANKING
GOOGLE	85th (2005)	14th (2012)
BARCLAYS CAPITAL	95th (2004)	28th (2011)
MI5 – THE SECURITY SERVICE	96th (2007)	33rd (2010)
ALDI	65th (2002)	3rd (2009)
JAGUAR LAND ROVER	87th (2009)	26th (2012)
TEACH FIRST	63rd (2004)	4th (2012)
ATKINS	94th (2004)	37th (2009)
LIDL	89th (2009)	32nd (2012)
ARCADIA GROUP	99th (2001)	47th (2007)
SLAUGHTER AND MAY	90th (2001)	39th (2010)

EMPLOYERS FALLING FURTHEST 1997-2012	HIGHEST RANKING	LOWEST RANKING
ICI	5th (1997)	Not ranked (2001, 2004, FROM 2006)
BRITISH AIRWAYS	6th (1999)	Not ranked (2010, 2011)
FORD	11th (1999)	Not ranked (FROM 2006)
REUTERS	22nd (2001)	Not ranked (FROM 2009)
ASTRAZENECA	24th (2003)	Not ranked (2002)
MINISTRY OF DEFENCE	35th (2003)	Not ranked (2007, 2012)
MARCONI	36th (2001)	Not ranked (FROM 2002)
DIAGEO	37th (2004)	Not ranked (2008-2009)
LOGICA	39th (1999)	Not ranked (FROM 2003)
QINETIQ	43rd (2001)	Not ranked (2007, 2011-2012)

Source High Fliers Research

The Top 10 Graduate Employers 1997-2011

1997
1. MARKS & SPENCER
2. PROCTER & GAMBLE
3. ARTHUR ANDERSEN
4. ANDERSEN CONSULTING (NOW ACCENTURE)
5. ICI
6. UNILEVER
7. BP
8. CIVIL SERVICE
9. SHELL
10. BOOTS

1998
1. ANDERSEN CONSULTING (NOW ACCENTURE)
2. ARTHUR ANDERSEN
3. PROCTER & GAMBLE
4. MARKS & SPENCER
5. CIVIL SERVICE
6. BOOTS
7. UNILEVER
8. KPMG
9. PRICE WATERHOUSE
10. BRITISH AIRWAYS

1999
1. ANDERSEN CONSULTING (NOW ACCENTURE)
2. ARTHUR ANDERSEN
3. PRICEWATERHOUSECOOPERS
4. PROCTER & GAMBLE
5. GOLDMAN SACHS
6. CIVIL SERVICE
7. KPMG
8. UNILEVER
9. ARMY
10. MARS

2000
1. ANDERSEN CONSULTING (NOW ACCENTURE)
2. PRICEWATERHOUSECOOPERS
3. ANDERSEN (FORMERLY ARTHUR ANDERSEN)
4. CIVIL SERVICE
5. ARMY
6. KPMG
7. UNILEVER
8. PROCTER & GAMBLE
9. GOLDMAN SACHS
10. MARS

2001
1. ACCENTURE
2. ARTHUR ANDERSEN
3. PRICEWATERHOUSECOOPERS
4. PROCTER & GAMBLE
5. GOLDMAN SACHS
6. CIVIL SERVICE
7. KPMG
8. UNILEVER
9. ARMY
10. MARS

2002
1. ACCENTURE
2. PRICEWATERHOUSECOOPERS
3. ANDERSEN (FORMERLY ARTHUR ANDERSEN)
4. CIVIL SERVICE
5. ARMY
6. KPMG
7. UNILEVER
8. PROCTER & GAMBLE
9. GOLDMAN SACHS
10. MARS

2003
1. CIVIL SERVICE
2. ACCENTURE
3. PRICEWATERHOUSECOOPERS
4. ARMY
5. KPMG
6. HSBC
7. BBC
8. PROCTER & GAMBLE
9. NHS
10. DELOITTE & TOUCHE (NOW DELOITTE)

2004
1. PRICEWATERHOUSECOOPERS
2. CIVIL SERVICE
3. ACCENTURE
4. KPMG
5. NHS
6. BBC
7. ARMY
8. PROCTER & GAMBLE
9. HSBC
10. DELOITTE

2005
1. PRICEWATERHOUSECOOPERS
2. CIVIL SERVICE
3. ACCENTURE
4. KPMG
5. BBC
6. DELOITTE
7. NHS
8. HSBC
9. GOLDMAN SACHS
10. PROCTER & GAMBLE

2006
1. PRICEWATERHOUSECOOPERS
2. DELOITTE
3. KPMG
4. CIVIL SERVICE
5. BBC
6. NHS
7. HSBC
8. ACCENTURE
9. PROCTER & GAMBLE
10. GOLDMAN SACHS

2007
1. PRICEWATERHOUSECOOPERS
2. DELOITTE
3. KPMG
4. CIVIL SERVICE
5. BBC
6. NHS
7. ACCENTURE
8. HSBC
9. ALDI
10. GOLDMAN SACHS

2008
1. PRICEWATERHOUSECOOPERS
2. DELOITTE
3. KPMG
4. ACCENTURE
5. NHS
6. CIVIL SERVICE
7. BBC
8. ALDI
9. TEACH FIRST
10. GOLDMAN SACHS

2009
1. PRICEWATERHOUSECOOPERS
2. DELOITTE
3. ALDI
4. CIVIL SERVICE
5. KPMG
6. NHS
7. ACCENTURE
8. TEACH FIRST
9. BBC
10. ERNST & YOUNG

2010
1. PRICEWATERHOUSECOOPERS
2. DELOITTE
3. CIVIL SERVICE
4. KPMG
5. ALDI
6. NHS
7. TEACH FIRST
8. ACCENTURE
9. BBC
10. ERNST & YOUNG

2011
1. PWC (FORMERLY PRICEWATERHOUSECOOPERS)
2. DELOITTE
3. KPMG
4. ALDI
5. NHS
6. BBC
7. TEACH FIRST
8. CIVIL SERVICE
9. ACCENTURE
10. ERNST & YOUNG

Source High Fliers Research

See yourself being part of one big team. Expect inspiration.

At Barclays, you will have the opportunity to work with colleagues who will inspire and support you as you build your career. Together, your ideas, ambition and talent have the power to drive the future of our business. We reward your commitment by offering you unparalleled training, support and global opportunities – because we see cultivating top talent as a critical business priority, not just a nice-to-have. So expect to be stretched. Expect to go further, faster and higher. And expect to have your potential fulfilled.

See yourself go further at barclays.com/seeyourself

Investment Bank

 **BARCLAYS**

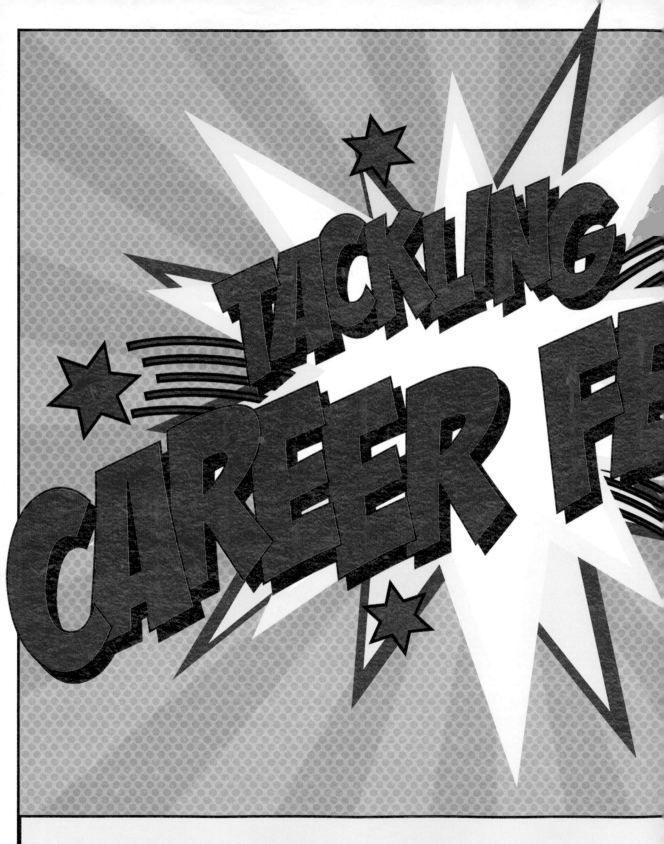

WE KNOW THINKING ABOUT YOUR CAREER CAN BE PRETTY DAUNTING. BUT WITH QUALITY ADVICE, GUIDANCE AND SUPPORT, PLUS THE LATEST OPPORTUNITIES WITH THE BEST GRADUATE EMPLOYERS, WE'LL SHOW YOU THERE'S NOTHING TO BE SCARED OF. VISIT THE MOST WIDELY USED GRADUATE RECRUITMENT WEBSITE, **MILKROUND.COM**

Celebrating Ten Years of Teach First

By **James Darley**
Director of Graduate Recruitment, Teach First

It's strange yet exciting to think that one of the organisations that is ranked within the top five of this year's edition of *The Times Top 100 Graduate Employers* launched just a decade ago – and that teaching in a school in challenging circumstances is now viewed as one of the most prestigious career options by the country's brightest university-leavers.

Since its launch in 2002, Teach First has changed the perceptions of top graduates throughout the UK and has become an influential charity and a movement for social change, focused on addressing an enduring and corrosive feature of UK society – educational disadvantage – by driving up standards and raising aspirations in primary and secondary schools in challenging circumstances.

It is a sad reality that in our country today, children who come from lower socio-economic backgrounds do not have the same access to opportunities for educational success as their wealthier neighbours, and this link between income and attainment in school is stronger in the UK than almost anywhere else in the developed world. An easier way to explain this inequity is the statistic from the Sutton Trust, a charity that aims to promote social mobility through education. Their data shows that 96% of children from private

> **❝** *In 2011, Ofsted rated Teach First's initial teacher training provision as 'outstanding' in all forty-four areas evaluated.* **❞**

schools go to university compared to just 16% on free schools meals. But why should family income result in an 80% difference in access to university?

Teach First believes this is more than unfair, it's unacceptable and thousands of people are doing something about it. Research shows that high-quality teaching has the power to undermine this correlation and provide children with the opportunity to fulfil their potential, regardless of their family's wealth.

Our programme helps to rapidly transform high-calibre graduates into inspiring teachers and leaders, providing skills, experiences and opportunities to begin making an immediate difference to children in the classroom, and to lay the foundations of an influential leadership career in any field.

At the heart of Teach First is a unique two-year leadership development programme which has been designed to help graduates develop the skills and behaviours that are needed to make a real difference to each student in the classroom.

Over the last ten years Teach First has evolved into a dynamic, effective and high profile organisation that transforms the life opportunities of the children and young people it reaches, and opens up new possibilities for the outstanding graduates who join.

DIVERSE, INTERNATIONAL AND COMMERCIALLY AWARE, WE WORK TOGETHER. TOGETHER WE ARE CLIFFORD CHANCE.

Joining us as a trainee means sharing our ambition and drive to set the pace among the global elite law firms. You will develop your potential as part of an exceptionally talented legal team, and tackle the issues and decisions that shape our clients' success – helping them to achieve competitive advantage in challenging business circumstances.

Find out about opportunities at Clifford Chance – a law firm built on collaboration, innovation and a relentless commitment to quality, and with more leading cross-border practices than any other firm *(Chambers Global 2012)*.

Together we are Clifford Chance.
www.cliffordchance.com/gradsuk

CLIFFORD CHANCE

Almost 1,000 graduates joined the Teach First programme in 2012

I joined Teach First nine years ago to head-up their graduate recruitment because I fundamentally believed then – as I do now – that a child's educational success should not be determined by their parents' income. I believe that we can change the face of education if the country's best graduates Teach First.

Even in those early days, we felt that if we could become an 'employer of choice' for top graduates and establish ourselves as the best option for the brightest and the best upon graduation, we could potentially unlock enormous growth and have real impact in schools.

Having started originally in London schools, Teach First began to grow nationally in 2005, through support from Government and corporate sponsorship and increased its annual intake of graduates from 183 to more than 260 for the first time. The charity stepped-up its promotions at universities and forged lasting partnerships with other top graduate employers, which helped build the credibility of the programme.

Teach First is now supported by leading organisations spanning all sectors. They recognise the importance of the work that we do and are keen to support our mission. Many also value the skills and experiences our graduates gain through our leadership development programme - they understand the leadership required in teaching and see its transferability to other roles.

Our evolution over the last five years has seen the number of graduates recruited for Teach First increase from 270 a year to almost 1,000 in 2012. We've done it by investing heavily in our graduate recruitment team, so that our recruiters can spend as much time as possible at key universities across the UK. Our aim has been to have recruiters on campus three or four days a week, to help the next generation of students understand what joining Teach First could mean for them.

The Teach First brand continues to grow and we have designed a highly student-focused recruitment model. Despite being among the UK's largest graduate recruiters, it usually takes just four or five weeks from submitting an application to receiving a job offer, one of the fastest recruitment processes of any graduate employer in the country.

We are immensely proud of the effect that Teach First is having on children's lives. On a pupil and school level there is visible change occurring, as hundreds of pupils who have gone through the HEAPS programme (Higher Education Access Programme for Schools) are now studying at university as the first in their family to do so and starting to join Teach First after graduation.

Many of the partner schools have undergone transformational change as well – at Uxbridge High School, for example, the proportion of pupils getting 5 A*-C at GSCE has risen from 29% in 2003 to 88% in 2010. The culture of many of the partner schools, such as Wembley High Technology College, have changed from being somewhere that university entrance was rare, to moving towards 100% of their sixth formers going to university each year, including some of the most selective universities in the country.

We place a very high priority on working with schools that are really committed to supporting our participants as they tackle the enormous challenges of developing as teachers in 'real time'.

In every school that we work with the headteacher has actively requested Teach First teachers and has undertaken to provide the right level of support for our graduates.

In 2011, Ofsted rated Teach First's initial teacher training provision 'outstanding' in all forty-four areas evaluated, and reported that "the quality of the participants is exceptional, particularly their personal characteristics…self-motivation, reflection and commitment… to addressing educational disadvantage."

At the end of their two years of teaching, Teach First participants become official 'ambassadors' for the programme, helping to support the future development of Teach First, either from within teaching – currently more than half of ambassadors are in teaching positions throughout the UK – or through their subsequent careers in business, the third sector and government. United by a unique insight into the challenges schools face, experience of what works, and the expertise and commitment to continue addressing the Teach First vision, this is a powerful network for social change.

This year marks the ten year anniversary of Teach First and whilst the charity can reflect on successes at both a pupil and school level, educational disadvantage still remains one of the most destructive and pervasive problems in the UK. Last year in England, just 34% of pupils on free school meals achieved 5 A*-C grades including English and Maths at GCSE, compared with 58% nationally.

Through the impact made by our participants, ambassadors and thousands of other teachers and school leaders in our partner schools over the past ten years we know that change is possible but there is still much more work to be done.

Teach First has ambitious plans to dramatically increase the impact and number of participants and ambassadors over the next three years. Growing to an intake of 2,000 graduates a year by 2015 will not only enable Teach First to reach 90% of challenging schools that serve low income pupils in England, but will also mean that we will represent a quarter of all new teachers in those Primary and Secondary schools and a third of all science, technology, engineering and mathematics teachers (the 'STEM' subjects) – this is a scale that can have a real impact.

In practical terms, this means doubling the size of Teach First in just three years, growing 50% larger than the next largest graduate recruiter and recruiting to a scale never done in the history of the graduate recruitment in the UK.

Teach First simply can't do this alone, doubling in size over the next three years will require many people to see and do things differently. Students have to be inspired to play their part in changing the future of school education for the better and parents must continue to show immense pride when their sons and daughters receive their offer to teach in a challenging school for two years.

And universities themselves will need to take responsibility for encouraging and supporting their next generation of graduates to Teach First after their degrees. This is starting to happen at a number of institutions – York, Nottingham, more than twenty colleges in Oxford, and six in Cambridge have launched innovative ways to fund and support more of their top students to join Teach First. Through these initiatives we are already showing that Teach First can be part of the solution to some of the current challenges that universities face – improving graduates' employability, widening access to degree courses, supporting local schools and communities, and even helping with the future survival of key degree subjects like chemistry, physics and mathematics.

Imagine too, the future influence of Teach First's growing number of ambassadors and their potential to deliver systemic change as they move into positions of influence across society. Our dream is to have a prime minister, government ministers, heads of schools, policy makers, heads of industry, newspaper editors and leaders of social enterprises who have all done Teach First and seen first-hand the injustice of educational disadvantage, who can then drive the fundamental changes needed to really deliver a fairer future.

Change can and will happen if we all want it to. I was privileged to visit Finland at the start of the year, a country that consistently tops the international league table for educational excellence. It is a country, of course with problems, but with a societal belief that education really matters. Education there is free for all, vocational and educational training are respected equally, and everyone is educated together by the state, without the need for private schools. What is fascinating is that equality has delivered excellence not the other way round, and what it clearly told me was that if society cares enough about education and engages,

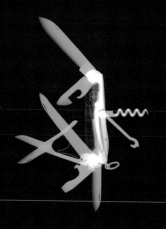

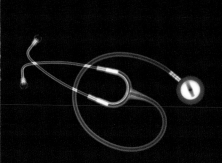

educational disadvantage is a fixable problem.

Teach First may only be ten years old but it has shown that the impossible can happen – the UK's most ambitious graduates now see teaching in a demanding school as an enviable career option after university. Children across the country from the most deprived backgrounds are starting to get access to inspirational teachers and leaders, and their life opportunities are being transformed by amazing graduates who care about each and every one of them.

A decade ago, you could count the number of Oxford and Cambridge graduates who went into teaching in challenging schools on one hand. Now, ten years on, 10% of all Oxbridge finalists and 6%

of all finalists from the Russell Group of leading universities apply to Teach First and we are one of, if not the, largest recruiter from many of the country's top universities.

Joining Teach First means that graduates can literally change young people's lives and help them to access a different future. It's already happening in primary and secondary schools up and down the country where over 4,300 Teach First participants have committed their energy, ideas and enthusiasm.

Being a teacher, becoming a leader, inspiring a future generation, making a difference – all in two years? It's a lot to take on board. Change their lives, and change yours. Teach First.

THE TIMES TOP 100 GRADUATE EMPLOYERS — Teach First's Recruitment & Ranking in the Top 100

Source High Fliers Research, Teach First

USE YOUR HEAD

CHOOSE A GRADUATE EMPLOYER
THAT'S IN THE TIMES TOP 100

FOLLOW YOUR HEART

BE PART OF AN ORGANISATION
THAT'S LEADING THE FIGHT
AGAINST CANCER

GRADUATE OPPORTUNITIES.

Cancer Research UK is an inspiring story about smart, brave
people who came together to beat cancer. Over the last
century, we've built an international reputation for excellence.
So, when you join us as a graduate, you won't just benefit
from training and development that's earned us a place in
the Times Top 100. You'll be following in the footsteps
of the industry's biggest talents – and shaping the growth
of the world's leading cancer charity dedicated to saving lives.

Find out more at graduates.cancerresearchuk.org

CANCER
RESEARCH
UK

Get The Times Digital Pack for half price

Our great-value Digital Pack is perfect for those who want their news on the move. Enjoy the award-winning iPad editions for The Times and The Sunday Times, access to both websites and our smartphone app for **just £2 a week for the first three months - saving 50%.** After three months access is just £4 a week.

Wherever you are, you'll be able to access a huge range of content, including videos, articles, live news and bulletins. Plus, online you can delve into The Times Archive, dating back to 1785.

The Digital Pack includes:

☑ The Times and The Sunday Times iPad editions

☑ Unlimited access to thetimes.co.uk and thesundaytimes.co.uk

☑ Complimentary access to The Times and The Sunday Times smartphone app

☑ Exclusive membership of Times+, including 2-for-1 cinema tickets at Cineworld every weekend

Call **0800 389 6893** quoting **'graduates'**

Visit **timespacks.com/graduates**

THE ⚜ TIMES

TOP 100

GRADUATE EMPLOYERS

Index

EMPLOYER	TOP 100 RANKING	ACCOUNTANCY	CONSULTING	ENGINEERING	FINANCE	GENERAL MANAGEMENT	HUMAN RESOURCES	INVESTMENT BANKING	IT	LAW	LOGISTICS	MARKETING	MEDIA	PROPERTY	PURCHASING	RESEARCH & DEVELOPMENT	RETAILING	SALES	NUMBER OF VACANCIES	PAGE
JOHN LEWIS PARTNERSHIP	10				●	●								●		●			40+	150
KPMG	3	●	●		●		●		●										800+	152
KRAFT FOODS	97			●	●						●	●			●			●	Around 20	154
L'ORÉAL	30				●							●	●					●	35	156
LIDL	32				●									●	●		●	●	20	158
LINKLATERS	43									●									110	160
LLOYD'S	95				●														11-12	162
LLOYDS BANKING GROUP	38				●	●	●	●	●										220	164
MARKS & SPENCER	28					●	●		●			●	●	●	●		●		20	166
MARS	60			●	●	●								●	●				Around 25	168
MCDONALD'S	55				●												●		100-150	170
MCKINSEY & COMPANY	40		●																No fixed quota	172
METROPOLITAN POLICE	79	●			●	●	●		●	●		●	●		●				To be confirmed	174
MI5	50				●	●	●		●	●									To be confirmed	176
MICROSOFT	33								●								●		45	178
MORGAN STANLEY	34				●		●	●	●										250-300	180
NATIONAL GRID	84	●		●	●	●			●		●			●	●	●			60+	182
NESTLÉ	47			●	●	●					●	●		●				●	50	184
NETWORK RAIL	51	●		●	●	●			●	●			●	●					100	186
NGDP	70				●														50+	188
NHS	6			●	●	●			●										Up to 150	190
NORTON ROSE	85									●									55	192
NUCLEARGRADUATES	66			●															45	194
OLIVER WYMAN	94		●																No fixed quota	196
OXFAM	86	●				●	●		●			●	●		●	●			50+ (voluntary)	198
PENGUIN	75	●			●		●				●	●	●			●			Around 30-50	200
PROCTER & GAMBLE	21	●		●	●		●		●		●	●			●		●		100	202
PWC	1	●	●		●				●	●									Around 1,200	204
ROLLS-ROYCE	25			●	●	●	●							●					400	206
ROYAL AIR FORCE	93			●	●	●			●		●								130+	208
ROYAL BANK OF SCOTLAND GROUP	22	●			●	●		●											500+	210
ROYAL NAVY	72			●	●	●			●	●	●				●				No fixed quota	212
SAINSBURY'S	39					●					●	●		●		●			20	214
SANTANDER	62				●	●										●			115	216
SAVILLS	89													●					50+	218
SHELL	35			●	●	●			●		●			●	●		●		100+	220
SKY	41	●	●		●	●	●		●		●	●	●	●					100	222
SLAUGHTER AND MAY	49									●									90	224
TEACH FIRST	4	●	●	●	●	●	●	●	●	●	●	●	●	●	●	●	●	●	1,260	226
TESCO	12			●	●	●			●		●	●	●	●	●		●		300	228
TOWERS WATSON	80		●		●	●			●										120-130	230
TRANSPORT FOR LONDON	82	●		●	●	●			●		●								Around 100	232
UBS	61	●			●		●	●	●										300+	234
UNILEVER	19			●	●		●		●			●			●	●			60-70	236
WPP	42											●	●						1-10	238

BE > YOUR DEGREE

accenture.com/top100

As a world-leading management consulting, technology services and outsourcing company, Accenture is the name behind the transformation of some of the world's best known businesses. For a career that will challenge and inspire, Accenture is an unmissable opportunity.

Unrivalled in state-of-the-art thinking and technological know-how, Accenture helps organisations in every sector achieve even higher performance. How? By spotting opportunities and delivering inspirational solutions that help clients move to the next level.

Accenture's influence reaches far and wide, changing the way organisations perform, and impacting on how the world interacts with technology. 50% of the planet's post is now processed using Accenture systems for example – while for anyone making an online payment today, chances are it'll be secured by Accenture technology.

High-performing graduates who join Accenture can expect a transformation of their own as they enjoy direct involvement with a broad spectrum of clients. Whether they're looking to specialise as a Consultant or a Technologist, new starters will be immersed in live projects from day one – while a structured programme of mentoring and learning will help them develop and grow beyond their imaginations. The encouragement and opportunities for personal and professional development are truly exceptional at Accenture, but it's up to graduates to make it happen.

Graduate opportunities are available across Consulting and Technology Solutions. For Consulting, a 2:1 in any discipline is welcome; for Technology Solutions, applicants will need a 2:1 in a technology, maths, science or engineering-related degree – and both require a genuine passion for technology.

BE > YOU IMAGINED

This is your invitation to join an organisation offering greater opportunity, greater challenge and greater satisfaction. An organisation dedicated to teamwork and collaboration. An organisation working in the forefront of technology, helping 92 of the Fortune Global 100 to reinvent business. Our capabilities are so broad, you can even change jobs without ever changing companies. Talk to Accenture and discover how great you can be.
Visit accenture.com/top100

BE GREATER THAN

accenture
High performance. Delivered.

www.airbus.com/work

facebook.com/airbuscareers **f**   airbusuk-grad@airbus.com ✕

Airbus is a leading aircraft manufacturer with the most modern and comprehensive family of airliners on the market. Over 11,600 Airbus aircraft have been sold to more than 330 customers worldwide and more than 7,000 of these have been delivered since the company first entered the market in the early seventies.

Airbus aircraft range in capacity from 100 to more than 500 seats: the single-aisle A320 Family, including A320neo, best selling aircraft in aviation history, the wide-body long-range A330 Family including the freighter and MRTT, and the all-new next generation A350 XWB Family and the double-deck A380 Family.

To stay at the top, Airbus needs dynamic graduates and talented undergraduates whose skills and potential are fully maximised. A vast range of career development opportunities are provided, including personal development strategies and training courses to enable each individual to plan their future career with the company.

Innovative graduates will enjoy the chance to develop their technical and leadership skills on the Airbus Direct Entry Graduate (DEG) Programme. A detailed knowledge of business functions will be gained through placements in the UK and Europe, with strategic partners, customers and suppliers. Involvement in education and community projects, to broaden personal and management skills, is also part of the programme.

For graduates looking for direct roles, Airbus has vacancies throughout the year in various disciplines in France, Germany, Spain and the UK.

At Airbus work-life balance through flexible working is actively promoted. Individuality is encouraged and diversity embraced. Airbus wants people to bring their own style and contribute to the richness of the organisation.

GRADUATE VACANCIES IN 2013
ENGINEERING
FINANCE
HUMAN RESOURCES
IT
LOGISTICS
PURCHASING
RESEARCH & DEVELOPMENT

NUMBER OF VACANCIES
50-80 graduate jobs

LOCATIONS OF VACANCIES

STARTING SALARY FOR 2013
£25,000
Plus a £2,750 welcome payment.

UNIVERSITY VISITS IN 2012-13
BATH, BRISTOL, CAMBRIDGE,
GLASGOW, IMPERIAL COLLEGE
LONDON, LIVERPOOL, LOUGHBOROUGH,
MANCHESTER, NOTTINGHAM, SHEFFIELD,
STRATHCLYDE, SWANSEA
Please check with your university careers service for full details of local events.

APPLICATION DEADLINE
31st December 2012

FURTHER INFORMATION
www.Top100GraduateEmployers.com
Register now for the latest news, events information and graduate recruitment details for Britain's leading employers.

GRADUATE VACANCIES IN 2013
GENERAL MANAGEMENT
RETAILING

NUMBER OF VACANCIES
100-125 graduate jobs

LOCATIONS OF VACANCIES

As one of the world's leading retailers, Aldi is renowned for attracting top quality, ambitious graduates who have a determination to succeed. In return for one of the best remuneration packages around, Aldi offers outstanding graduates real responsibility from day one.

Only the very best candidates are selected, and their ability to inspire, lead and motivate in the fast-paced environment which has made Aldi a driving force in retail is a vital prerequisite for all our managers.

Aldi Area Managers must be team players; Aldi actively seeks out graduates who have already gained leadership experience, either in their academic or personal lives. The initiative and skills required to lead a local or university team, undertake voluntary work, take a gap year or strive for personal excellence are favoured over first-class honours. Aldi is looking for self-starters who have confidence in their ability to shine.

Candidates who are selected for the Management Programme begin their journey in-store and within weeks will be managing a store of their own. Aldi expects excellence and attention to detail, and in return offers fast-track career progression and real responsibility.

After receiving thorough training in all aspects of retail management, from store operations through to financial administration, Aldi's graduate trainees are given the skills to take charge of a multi-million pound area of 3 to 4 stores to run, as and when they are ready.

To be successful, graduates will need good academics, high energy levels, a willingness to learn and the determination to overcome the challenges ahead. In return Aldi offers an excellent starting salary and a fully expensed Audi A4 is also included within the package.

STARTING SALARY FOR 2013
£40,000

UNIVERSITY VISITS IN 2012-13
ABERDEEN, ASTON, BATH, BIRMINGHAM, BRISTOL, CARDIFF, DUNDEE, DURHAM, EDINBURGH, ESSEX, EXETER, GLASGOW, LEEDS, LIVERPOOL, LOUGHBOROUGH, MANCHESTER, NEWCASTLE, NORTHUMBRIA, NOTTINGHAM, READING, SHEFFIELD, SOUTHAMPTON, ST ANDREWS, STIRLING, STRATHCLYDE, WARWICK
Please check with your university careers service for full details of local events.

MINIMUM ENTRY REQUIREMENTS
2.1 Degree

APPLICATION DEADLINE
Year-round recruitment

FURTHER INFORMATION
www.Top100GraduateEmployers.com
Register now for the latest news, events information and graduate recruitment details for Britain's leading employers.

The thing that means you don't just make the team, you captain it.

We want it.

The kind of person you are really determines if you can make it onto one of the most challenging, rewarding and sought-after graduate training programmes in the UK. Qualifications are important, but determination, competitiveness and team skills are vital. Within a few months you could be managing three to four Aldi stores, so you'll also need to be able to take on real responsibility. If you're motivated and ambitious, then you never know; one day you might wake up realising you've landed a career that is second to none.

Graduate Area Manager £40,000 rising to £63,500 after 4 years.

Fully expensed Audi A4.
Opportunity for directorship within 5 years.
International secondment opportunities.

aldirecruitment.co.uk/tt100

 Apply yourself here.

ALLEN & OVERY

www.allenovery.com/careeruk

facebook.com/allenoverygrads **f**   graduate.recruitment@allenovery.com ✉

Allen & Overy LLP is an international legal practice with approximately 5,000 people in 42 major centres worldwide. The practice's client list includes many of the world's top businesses, financial institutions and governments, and naturally, the firm is committed to providing innovative, high quality advice to them.

Allen & Overy is world renowned for the high quality of its banking, corporate and international capital markets advice, but also has major strengths in litigation and dispute resolution, employment and benefits, tax and real estate.

Within its broad range of expertise, the practice offers a training contract characterised by flexibility and choice. Training contracts are tailored for each trainee to ensure they have the best start to their career. Given the strength of Allen & Overy's international finance practice, trainees spend at least 12 months working in banking, corporate and international capital markets. There are also opportunities for trainees to undertake an international or client secondment in their second year of training. By working closely with partners and other colleagues, trainees develop practical experience and enjoy a high level of early responsibility.

Vital to Allen & Overy's success is the way they approach work. Allen & Overy people enjoy what they do and want to employ individuals who can use their initiative while maintaining a professional, supportive and friendly working environment.

Allen & Overy recruits 90 trainee solicitors and 60 vacation students (winter and summer) each year. Applications are welcome from both law and non-law candidates. Good academics are essential, along with evidence of teamwork, leadership, motivation and problem-solving demonstrated.

GRADUATE VACANCIES IN 2013
LAW

NUMBER OF VACANCIES
90 graduate jobs
For training contracts starting in 2015.

LOCATIONS OF VACANCIES

STARTING SALARY FOR 2013
£38,000

UNIVERSITY VISITS IN 2012-13
BATH, BELFAST, BIRMINGHAM, BRISTOL, BRUNEL, CAMBRIDGE, CARDIFF, CITY, DURHAM, EAST ANGLIA, EDINBURGH, EXETER, IMPERIAL COLLEGE LONDON, KEELE, KING'S COLLEGE LONDON, LANCASTER, LEEDS, LEICESTER, LONDON SCHOOL OF ECONOMICS, LOUGHBOROUGH, MANCHESTER, NEWCASTLE, NOTTINGHAM, OXFORD, QUEEN MARY LONDON, READING, ROYAL HOLLOWAY LONDON, SCHOOL OF AFRICAN STUDIES, SHEFFIELD, SOUTHAMPTON, ST ANDREWS, TRINITY COLLEGE DUBLIN, UNIVERSITY COLLEGE DUBLIN, UNIVERSITY COLLEGE LONDON, WARWICK, YORK
Please check with your university careers service for full details of local events.

MINIMUM ENTRY REQUIREMENTS
2.1 Degree

APPLICATION DEADLINE
Please see website for full details.

FURTHER INFORMATION
www.Top100GraduateEmployers.com
Register now for the latest news, events information and graduate recruitment details for Britain's leading employers.

ALLEN & OVERY

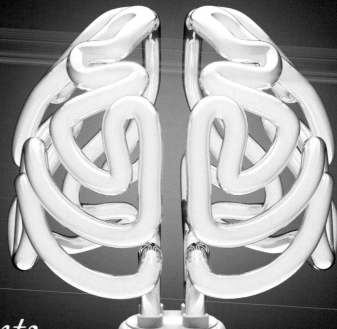

Setting precedents, not following them.

At Allen & Overy you will have to be able to think beyond what has been done before. You'll be supporting ambitious businesses that are themselves breaking new ground and your ideas can make the difference. So, from your first day as a trainee – and even as a student on a vacation scheme – what you do and say will matter, both to your team and to your clients.

Visit **www.allenovery.com/careeruk** to see more.

Join Allen & Overy to do more.

www.facebook.com/AllenOveryGrads

Allen & Overy means Allen & Overy LLP and/or its affiliated undertakings

BHS

BURTON

DOROTHY PERKINS

EVANS

OUTFIT

TOPSHOP

TOPMAN

wallis

Arcadia Group is the UK's largest privately owned fashion retailer with over 45,000 employees in more than 30 countries. Arcadia's portfolio of brands include eight of the high street best known fashion brands – Burton, Dorothy Perkins, Evans, Miss Selfridge, Topman, Topshop, Bhs and Wallis – along with the shopping concept Outfit.

Arcadia's graduate recruits provide invaluable support to the business in Buying and Merchandising roles, as well as Group roles such as Finance and E-commerce. Successful graduates come from a variety of degree backgrounds and benefit from direct, on-the-job training that ensures they are provided with real skills and real responsibilities right from day one.

By providing them with the tools to manage their own careers, and encouraging them to move between the nine brands and Group Functions, Arcadia is known for having one of the most experienced and rounded workforces in the industry.

Arcadia recruits all year round and looks for passionate, self-motivated, enthusiastic individuals who are focussed on a career in retail and will add a different perspective to the business. In return graduates are offered a breadth of opportunity and the scope to develop their career in the knowledge that they are working for one of the most inspirational fashion retailers in the industry.

After the initial application, graduates will be invited to a telephone interview and those who are successful will then participate in a face to face assessment where brand/department fit is identified.

Graduates are rewarded with a competitive salary, up to 25 days holiday, bonus, membership of the group pension scheme, sponsorship of professional qualifications and an attractive 25% discount on products from Arcadia stores!

GRADUATE VACANCIES IN 2013

FINANCE
LOGISTICS
PURCHASING
RETAILING

NUMBER OF VACANCIES
300 graduate jobs

LOCATIONS OF VACANCIES

STARTING SALARY FOR 2013
£19,000+
Plus a company bonus.

UNIVERSITY VISITS IN 2012-13
Please check with your university careers service for full details of local events.

MINIMUM ENTRY REQUIREMENTS
Dependent on position
Please see website for full details.

APPLICATION DEADLINE
Year-round recruitment

FURTHER INFORMATION
www.Top100GraduateEmployers.com
Register now for the latest news, events information and graduate recruitment details for Britain's leading employers.

Arcadia

CAREERS THAT SET THE TREND

For further information about our vacancies,
visit: www.arcadiagroup.co.uk/careers

ARMY
BE THE BEST
REGULAR & TERRITORIAL

www.army.mod.uk/jobs

Being an Army Officer is a graduate career with a difference – from commanding a platoon of over 30 soldiers preparing for operations one week to organising a team training event the next, the British Army trains graduates to become some of the best leaders in the world.

As one of the largest most respected graduate employers, the Army offers unrivalled training and development to graduates of all disciplines, enhancing management and leadership potential and providing the skills and self-confidence to excel in the Army and, later on, in other careers. The Army is looking for people with leadership potential, a strong sense of moral direction and the resourcefulness to succeed.

Graduates start their Officer training at the Royal Military Academy Sandhurst (RMAS) where they learn all aspects of soldiering, as well as gain transferable skills in communication and leadership.

On completion of training at RMAS, they will join their Regiment or Corps where they will undergo further specialist training for their chosen occupation. Subsequently, Officers can also choose to study for recognised qualifications to further boost their CVs.

As well as offering variety, the Army offers continuous professional learning opportunities, great promotional prospects, unrivalled travel, sporting and adventure opportunities as well as benefits such as competitive pay and six weeks paid holiday per year.

The Army has approximately 650 graduate officer vacancies per annum, graduates should search 'Army jobs' to find out if they have got what it takes for a career in the Army. The Graduate offer salary is £29,586 on completion of training with good promotional prospects to follow.

GRADUATE VACANCIES IN 2013
ENGINEERING
FINANCE
GENERAL MANAGEMENT
HUMAN RESOURCES
IT
LOGISTICS

NUMBER OF VACANCIES
650 graduate jobs

LOCATIONS OF VACANCIES

STARTING SALARY FOR 2013
£24,615

UNIVERSITY VISITS IN 2012-13
Please check with your university careers service for full details of local events.

APPLICATION DEADLINE
Year-round recruitment

FURTHER INFORMATION
www.Top100GraduateEmployers.com
Register now for the latest news, events information and graduate recruitment details for Britain's leading employers.

WHERE TO NEXT?

They'll look to you for guidance.
They'll look to you for strength.
They'll put themselves in your hands.
Are you ready to lead?
Are you ready?

Search Army Jobs

ARMY
BE THE BEST
REGULAR & TERRITORIAL

ARUP

An independent firm offering a broad range of professional services, Arup believes that by bringing great people together, great things will happen. With experts in design, engineering, planning, business consultancy, project management and much more, Arup people work together to shape a better world.

Arup has offices in more than 30 countries across the world, making international team-working part of everyday life and bringing together professionals from diverse disciplines and with complementary skills on a uniquely global scale.

The firm is owned in trust for Arup's employees and this independence translates through the thoughts and actions of its people. Operating principles and commitment to sustainability are paramount and Arup strives not only to embrace this in projects, but also to embed it into everyday thinking and working.

Graduate opportunities span a wide range of disciplines and offer exceptional experience for future leaders who are ambitious, organised and have outstanding communication skills. Arup's diversity helps to foster the creativity that is its hallmark; and the support and freedom for innovation that is encouraged has made Arup the driving force behind some of the most iconic and sustainable designs in the world.

Arup offers competitive benefits and continuous professional development built around employees and their ambitions. Graduates can undertake a professional training programme, accredited by leading organisations such as the Institution of Civil Engineers and the Association for Project Management.

As a firm, Arup seeks exceptional people with fresh ideas and curious minds who want to make a real difference to the environment we live in; passion, drive and creativity are a must.

GRADUATE VACANCIES IN 2013
CONSULTING
ENGINEERING
PROPERTY

NUMBER OF VACANCIES
100+ graduate jobs

LOCATIONS OF VACANCIES

STARTING SALARY FOR 2013
£Competitive
Plus a 'settling-in' allowance of £2,000-£4,000.

UNIVERSITY VISITS IN 2012-13
BATH, BELFAST, BIRMINGHAM, BRISTOL, CAMBRIDGE, CARDIFF, DURHAM, EDINBURGH, GLASGOW, HERIOT-WATT, IMPERIAL COLLEGE LONDON, LEEDS, LIVERPOOL, LOUGHBOROUGH, MANCHESTER, NEWCASTLE, NOTTINGHAM, OXFORD, SHEFFIELD, SOUTHAMPTON, ST ANDREWS, STRATHCLYDE, SWANSEA, UNIVERSITY COLLEGE LONDON, WARWICK, YORK
Please check with your university careers service for full details of local events.

MINIMUM ENTRY REQUIREMENTS
2.1 Degree
Relevant degree required for some roles.

APPLICATION DEADLINE
Year-round recruitment
Early application advised.

FURTHER INFORMATION
www.Top100GraduateEmployers.com
Register now for the latest news, events information and graduate recruitment details for Britain's leading employers.

"For me, it's the structure and **ethos** of the firm that sets **ARUP** apart from it's competitors

Its **Independence** has allowed it to **adapt** to an **ever changing** industry and its **culture** creates a **stimulating** working environment which I really **enjoy** being a part of"

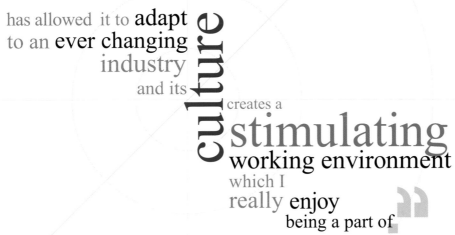

Jenny Pattison, Graduate Engineer

ARUP

[THIS IS BIG]

Asda is a multi-billion pound business with up to 200,000 colleagues working in over 500 stores and 24 depots. Part of the wider Walmart Group, the world's largest retailer, the organisation is an impressively large graduate employer in the UK with a highly successful Graduate Programme.

Added to this, Asda offers apprenticeships, placements, direct entry roles and more graduate opportunities through George.

In tough economic times, many companies task their graduates with making millions for their shareholders, while their customers continue to struggle. At Asda, the challenge is altogether different. Asda's mission is to help its 19 million customers save money every day, by striving to constantly drive down cost.

Asda has a proven record of developing outstanding business leaders, achieved through a culture where 'Every Day Matters' – where every day is seen as a development opportunity and where every individual colleague counts. Asda's philosophy "hire for attitude and train for skill" means they reward performance rather than background or academic achievement and welcome applicants from all degree disciplines. To succeed as part of the Graduate Programme, applicants need high levels of strategic and analytical drive, combined with a bright, pro-active approach and an entrepreneurial spirit.

Asda's Graduate Programmes cover Retail Management, Customer Service, Store Development, Distribution, Trading (Buying), Finance, HR, IT Solutions Management, Ecommerce (Digital), Supply and Marketing. In return for saving customers money every day, high performers can look forward to responsibility from day one, along with the prospect of being fast-tracked through a business where graduates are developed into future leaders, within Asda and beyond.

GRADUATE VACANCIES IN 2013
FINANCE
HUMAN RESOURCES
IT
LOGISTICS
MARKETING
PROPERTY
PURCHASING
RETAILING

NUMBER OF VACANCIES
Around 80 graduate jobs

LOCATIONS OF VACANCIES

STARTING SALARY FOR 2013
£Competitive
Plus benefits.

UNIVERSITY VISITS IN 2012-13
ASTON, BATH, BELFAST, BIRMINGHAM, BRISTOL, CAMBRIDGE, CARDIFF, DURHAM, EDINBURGH, EXETER, GLASGOW, IMPERIAL COLLEGE LONDON, KING'S COLLEGE LONDON, LANCASTER, LEEDS, LIVERPOOL, LONDON SCHOOL OF ECONOMICS, LOUGHBOROUGH, MANCHESTER, NEWCASTLE, NOTTINGHAM, OXFORD, READING, SHEFFIELD, SOUTHAMPTON, ST ANDREWS, STRATHCLYDE, UNIVERSITY COLLEGE LONDON, WARWICK, YORK
Please check with your university careers service for full details of local events.

MINIMUM ENTRY REQUIREMENTS
2.1 Degree

APPLICATION DEADLINE
31st December 2012

FURTHER INFORMATION
www.Top100GraduateEmployers.com
Register now for the latest news, events information and graduate recruitment details for Britain's leading employers.

www.ASDA.jobs/graduates

ASDA GRADUATE
PROGRAMME 2013

THE BIG BUSINESS
WITH BIG CHALLENGES
FOR GRADUATES WITH BIG AMBITIONS

ASDA
SAVING
YOU MONEY EVERY DAY

A refreshing new era is dawning.

The global economy has lost its shine.

It's time to wake up to a new way of working.

In a business that values every single penny.

Making money has always been easy.

Only the very brightest can save it.

ATKINS

GRADUATE VACANCIES IN 2013

CONSULTING

ENGINEERING

IT

PROPERTY

NUMBER OF VACANCIES
250+ graduate jobs

LOCATIONS OF VACANCIES

Vacancies also available in the USA, Asia and elsewhere in the world.

STARTING SALARY FOR 2013
£22,000-£33,000
Plus £2,500 Golden Hello and £2,500 upon completion of Chartership.

UNIVERSITY VISITS IN 2012-13
ABERDEEN, BATH, BRISTOL, CAMBRIDGE, CARDIFF, GLASGOW, HERIOT-WATT, IMPERIAL COLLEGE LONDON, LEEDS, LIVERPOOL, LOUGHBOROUGH, MANCHESTER, NEWCASTLE, NOTTINGHAM, NOTTINGHAM TRENT, OXFORD, SHEFFIELD, STRATHCLYDE, SURREY
Please check with your university careers service for full details of local events.

MINIMUM ENTRY REQUIREMENTS
2.1 Degree

APPLICATION DEADLINE
Year-round recruitment
Early application advised.

FURTHER INFORMATION
www.Top100GraduateEmployers.com
Register now for the latest news, events information and graduate recruitment details for Britain's leading employers.

Atkins is one of the world's leading engineering and design consultancies with a reputation for delivering iconic and innovative projects and developing people to be the best. It's a leader in many areas, including pioneering Carbon Critical Design, and is involved in growth industries around the world such as defence, aerospace and energy.

Atkins has the breadth and depth of expertise to respond to the most technically challenging and time-critical infrastructure projects. As the official engineering design services provider for the London 2012 Games, Atkins demonstrated its people's excellent technical ability to plan, design and enable world-class infrastructure projects.

Atkins is recruiting bright ambitious graduates to join in its 75th anniversary year. Applicants should enjoy addressing challenges with creative thinking – they will also demonstrate flexibility, resilience and drive.

Atkins offers an environment in which engineers, planners, architects and a myriad of related professionals flourish. Working for the largest UK employer in the engineering and design sector, Atkins' graduates have access to extensive opportunities across a range of geographical locations, functional disciplines and business areas. The scope for working on interesting and acclaimed projects – with inspiring colleagues – is high.

Atkins encourages graduates to drive their own development within a supportive and technically excellent team environment. The company's Graduate Development Programme combines mentoring, on-project experience, graduate forums and events. It also allows each graduate to follow a path that is unique, working towards personal and professional career goals and obtaining relevant Chartership qualifications.

BAE SYSTEMS

www.baesystems.com/Graduates

When looking for high performance, nothing beats the systems found in nature. Three billion years of evolution. That's the inspiration behind so much of what BAE Systems does. Join the company and become part of Europe's largest defence, security and aerospace company.

BAE Systems develops, delivers and supports some of the most advanced defence, security aerospace systems in the world. So whether it's military aircraft, surface ships, submarines or radar systems, BAE Systems makes it happen. For graduates, few organisations can offer opportunities as exciting and challenging in the fields of business, engineering and finance.

BAE Systems' main, two-year scheme is the Graduate Development Framework, which is split into business and engineering disciplines. Those who join the engineering area will continue to form the foundation of this business. BAE Systems have over 18,000 engineers in the UK; they look after the design, development, testing and production of over 100 new inventions each year, as well as a number of best-in-class products. However, just as vital to the business is ensuring that £multi-billion projects are delivered both efficiently and effectively. That's why outstanding performers are essential in the company's business graduate programme.

In addition to this, BAE Systems also has the Finance Leader Development Programme. This is a five-year fast-track graduate scheme, which seeks to prepare individuals to become Finance Directors of the future. The programme includes a structured and fully supported route to the highly respected Chartered Institute of Management Accountants (CIMA) qualification. It will also equip graduates with all the leadership and management skills necessary to become one of the finance function's senior leaders.

GRADUATE VACANCIES IN 2013
ACCOUNTANCY
ENGINEERING
FINANCE
GENERAL MANAGEMENT
HUMAN RESOURCES
IT
MARKETING
PURCHASING
RESEARCH & DEVELOPMENT

NUMBER OF VACANCIES
150 graduate jobs

LOCATIONS OF VACANCIES

STARTING SALARY FOR 2013
£24,000-£28,000
Golden Hello and pension scheme.

UNIVERSITY VISITS IN 2012-13
BATH, BELFAST, BRISTOL, BRUNEL, CARDIFF, DURHAM, EDINBURGH, GLASGOW, IMPERIAL COLLEGE LONDON, KENT, LANCASTER, LEEDS, LIVERPOOL, LOUGHBOROUGH, MANCHESTER, NEWCASTLE, NOTTINGHAM, SHEFFIELD, SOUTHAMPTON, STRATHCLYDE, SURREY, UNIVERSITY COLLEGE LONDON, WARWICK, YORK
Please check with your university careers service for full details of local events.

MINIMUM ENTRY REQUIREMENTS
2.1 Degree
Relevant degree required for some roles.

APPLICATION DEADLINE
Year-round recruitment
Early application advised.

FURTHER INFORMATION
www.Top100GraduateEmployers.com
Register now for the latest news, events information and graduate recruitment details for Britain's leading employers.

CALLING ALL OF NATURE'S GREAT PERFORMERS.

The dolphin. The ultimate listening device. Inspired by a dolphin's sonar, our Astute submarine sonar system has the world's largest number of hydrophones, giving it the biggest ears of any sonar system in service today. In fact, the perfect performance in nature is a great source of inspiration for our people, who are always looking to develop the most effective defence, aerospace and security systems on earth.

BUSINESS | **ENGINEERING** | **FINANCE**

baesystems.com/graduates

BAE SYSTEMS

REAL PERFORMANCE. REAL ADVANTAGE.

Bank of America Merrill Lynch

Bank of America is one of the world's largest financial institutions, serving individual consumers, small and middle-market businesses and large corporations with a full range of banking, investing, asset management and other financial and risk management products and services.

Bank of America Merrill Lynch is the marketing name for the global banking and global markets businesses. The company is a long-established participant in the European marketplace, with a presence since 1922. With offices throughout Europe and CEEMEA (Central Eastern Europe, the Middle East and Africa), Bank of America Merrill Lynch combines the best of local knowledge and international expertise, to offer its clients bespoke solutions no matter their location.

Full-time and internship programmes are available in the following areas: Global Markets, Investment Banking, Capital Markets, Corporate Banking, Global Treasury Solutions, Wealth Management, Research, International Corporate Treasury, Risk, Compliance, Technology, Quantitative Management and Human Resources. Graduates will gain a breadth of knowledge and experience and be positioned for great career opportunities.

Bank of America Merrill Lynch encourages a diverse, inclusive workplace. This gives the business the advantage of understanding and meeting the needs of diverse clients and shareholders, and provides fresh ideas and perspectives, which promote ingenuity. By joining Bank of America Merrill Lynch, graduates will receive the highest level of training and mentoring support. Furthermore, their commitment to improving the quality of life within the local community and taking care of the environment means they can get involved in a number of volunteering initiatives.

GRADUATE VACANCIES IN 2013
FINANCE
HUMAN RESOURCES
INVESTMENT BANKING
IT

NUMBER OF VACANCIES
250 graduate jobs

LOCATIONS OF VACANCIES

Vacancies also available in Europe and elsewhere in the world.

STARTING SALARY FOR 2013
£Competitive

UNIVERSITY VISITS IN 2012-13
BATH, BRISTOL, CAMBRIDGE, DURHAM, EDINBURGH, IMPERIAL COLLEGE LONDON, LONDON SCHOOL OF ECONOMICS, MANCHESTER, OXFORD, SHEFFIELD, SOUTHAMPTON, ST ANDREWS, UNIVERSITY COLLEGE LONDON, WARWICK
Please check with your university careers service for full details of local events.

MINIMUM ENTRY REQUIREMENTS
2.1 Degree
Relevant degree required for some roles.

APPLICATION DEADLINE
Please see website for full details.

FURTHER INFORMATION
www.Top100GraduateEmployers.com
Register now for the latest news, events information and graduate recruitment details for Britain's leading employers.

momentum

Set opportunity in motion
Careers in Europe, the Middle East & Africa

Face challenges with confidence. Nimbly navigate every obstacle in your path. It's that unique quality that's positioned you where you are today. And it's what we value at Bank of America Merrill Lynch. Join our team, and we'll open your career path and give you new opportunities to take the possible and make it real. We'll solicit your input and provide training, mentorship, and support to boost your aspirations to a global level. And as part of the world's leading financial institution, you can create the kind of opportunity that begets greater opportunity and bigger impact than you ever imagined.

seemore-bemore.com/TT100

facebook.com/BarclaysGraduates f   barclaysrecruitment@tmpw.co.uk ✕

youtube.com/barclaysgraduates ▶   twitter.com/barclaysgrads ⌄

BARCLAYS

Barclays is one of the world's leading banks, with 140,000 colleagues in over 50 countries and more than 48 million customers. But this business is not simply about scale. This is a global financial services organisation focused on creating and delivering the banking services of the future, to customers around the world.

Barclays Retail and Business Banking (RBB) stands out for its commitment to customers, its drive for innovation and its focus on people. The Future Leaders Development Programme (FLDP) has been created to help high-performing graduates become leaders of the business. It focuses on providing breadth and depth of experience and expertise, through rotations, formal training, mentoring and e-learning. From there, development is no less demanding: there are clear pathways to senior management for those with the leadership skills to succeed.

The FLDP opens up opportunities for graduates who want a global leadership career. Programmes include: Human Resources, Marketing & Products, Marketing Analytics, Technology Product and Process, Risk and Finance. In addition, the flagship Retail and Business Banking Leadership Programme offers far-reaching business experience and detailed customer insights to help you progress to the top of the retail banking world.

Throughout the two-year development programme, graduates will have access to a variety of learning resources and leadership initiatives. These include talks from senior managers, online tools, training modules – from emotional intelligence to organisational savvy – competitions and projects to stretch everyone, and a social network internally to share and collaborate. Graduates will need a strong academic record, work experience and most importantly, the evidence that they have the potential and desire to be a Future Leader.

GRADUATE VACANCIES IN 2013

ACCOUNTANCY
FINANCE
GENERAL MANAGEMENT
HUMAN RESOURCES
IT
MARKETING
RETAILING

NUMBER OF VACANCIES
100+ graduate jobs

LOCATIONS OF VACANCIES

Vacancies also available in Europe and elsewhere in the world.

STARTING SALARY FOR 2013
£36,000
Plus an £8,000 initial bonus.

UNIVERSITY VISITS IN 2012-13
ASTON, BATH, BIRMINGHAM, BRISTOL, CAMBRIDGE, CITY, DURHAM, EDINBURGH, GLASGOW, IMPERIAL COLLEGE LONDON, LANCASTER, LEEDS, LONDON SCHOOL OF ECONOMICS, LOUGHBOROUGH, MANCHESTER, NEWCASTLE, NOTTINGHAM, OXFORD, SHEFFIELD, SOUTHAMPTON, STRATHCLYDE, UNIVERSITY COLLEGE LONDON, WARWICK, YORK
Please check with your university careers service for full details of local events.

MINIMUM ENTRY REQUIREMENTS
2.1 Degree
300 UCAS points

APPLICATION DEADLINE
31st December 2012

FURTHER INFORMATION
www.Top100GraduateEmployers.com
Register now for the latest news, events information and graduate recruitment details for Britain's leading employers.

See more. Be more.

Future Leaders Development Programme

Barclays Retail and Business Banking has created the Future Leaders Development Programme for one purpose alone – to develop the Future Leaders of Barclays. From the quality of the induction, to the investment in development, from the innovative learning delivery, to the exposure to senior management – everything is focused on helping high-performing graduates become leaders in this global financial services organisation.

See more. Be more. Visit **seemore-bemore.com/TT100** to learn more.

Talk and follow us at

@barclaysgrads   f Barclays Graduates

Retail and Business Banking

BARCLAYS

www.barclays.com/seeyourself

See yourself being part of one big team. Expect inspiration.

With over 300 years in banking, Barclays operates in over 50 countries and employs 140,000 people worldwide. Through its Investment Bank, Barclays provides large corporate, government and institutional clients with solutions to their strategic advisory, financing and risk management needs.

Graduate and internship opportunities are available across the Investment Bank, from front-office areas such as Investment Banking, Trading and Sales, to specialist support functions like Human Resources, Technology and Operations. Barclays hires ambitious and analytical graduates from all degree disciplines although some roles, such as Technology, can require a specific qualification.

The Graduate Programme is Barclays key future talent stream and new joiners will typically enjoy early exposure to business-critical projects, gaining experience as they work alongside senior managers as valued members of the team. The programme kicks off with a comprehensive introduction to Barclays products and services, offering a thorough grounding in the financial markets, and continues with a range of presentations, case studies and workshops. Graduates can also expect to undertake role-specific training and one-on-one mentoring.

More graduates are recruited through internships than any other route. They generally last for 10-12 weeks over the summer and offer the opportunity to gain real experience in a real role, working on anything from live transactions and marketing projects to research and analysis, according to the business area.

The Spring Programme offers first-year students (or second year students on four-year courses) an intensive week of work shadowing, workshops, interactive skill sessions and numerous networking opportunities. All Spring Programme participants are automatically fast-tracked through to an assessment centre for a summer internship the following year.

GRADUATE VACANCIES IN 2013
FINANCE
HUMAN RESOURCES
INVESTMENT BANKING
IT
MARKETING

NUMBER OF VACANCIES
250 graduate jobs

LOCATIONS OF VACANCIES

STARTING SALARY FOR 2013
£Competitive

UNIVERSITY VISITS IN 2012-13
BATH, BRISTOL, CAMBRIDGE, DURHAM, EDINBURGH, GLASGOW, IMPERIAL COLLEGE LONDON, KING'S COLLEGE LONDON, LONDON SCHOOL OF ECONOMICS, LOUGHBOROUGH, MANCHESTER, NOTTINGHAM, OXFORD, STRATHCLYDE, WARWICK
Please check with your university careers service for full details of local events.

MINIMUM ENTRY REQUIREMENTS
2.1 Degree

APPLICATION DEADLINE
15th November 2012

FURTHER INFORMATION
www.Top100GraduateEmployers.com
Register now for the latest news, events information and graduate recruitment details for Britain's leading employers.

See yourself moving onward and upward. Expect opportunities.

At Barclays, your unleashed potential is our most powerful asset. Your ideas, ambition and talent have the power to drive the future of our business. We reward your commitment by offering you unparalleled training, support and global opportunities – because we see cultivating top talent as a critical business priority, not just a nice-to-have. So expect to be stretched. Expect to go further, faster and higher. And expect to have your potential fulfilled.

Exceed your expectations at barclays.com/seeyourself

Investment Bank

www.bdo.co.uk/graduates

student.recruitment@bdo.co.uk

twitter.com/BDO_trainees   facebook.com/BDOtrainees

GRADUATE VACANCIES IN 2013
ACCOUNTANCY
FINANCE

NUMBER OF VACANCIES
Around 200 graduate jobs

LOCATIONS OF VACANCIES

STARTING SALARY FOR 2013
£Competitive

UNIVERSITY VISITS IN 2012-13
ASTON, BATH, BIRMINGHAM, BRISTOL,
CAMBRIDGE, CARDIFF, CITY, DURHAM,
EDINBURGH, ESSEX, EXETER, GLASGOW,
IMPERIAL COLLEGE LONDON, KING'S
COLLEGE LONDON, LANCASTER,
LEEDS, LIVERPOOL, LONDON SCHOOL
OF ECONOMICS, LOUGHBOROUGH,
MANCHESTER, NEWCASTLE, NOTTINGHAM,
OXFORD, QUEEN MARY LONDON, READING,
SCHOOL OF AFRICAN STUDIES, SHEFFIELD,
SOUTHAMPTON, STRATHCLYDE, SURREY,
SUSSEX, UNIVERSITY COLLEGE LONDON,
WARWICK, YORK
*Please check with your university careers
service for full details of local events.*

MINIMUM ENTRY REQUIREMENTS
2.1 Degree
280 UCAS points

APPLICATION DEADLINE
Early application advised.

FURTHER INFORMATION
www.Top100GraduateEmployers.com
*Register now for the latest news, events
information and graduate recruitment
details for Britain's leading employers.*

Not all big accountancy firms are the same. BDO is building a strikingly different business, focused on exceptional client service. It employs exceptional people – and helps them to get on with the job, without needless bureaucracy. Its systems work to support its people, not the other way around.

The firm is looking for graduates who don't fit the conventional accountancy mould. Talented people with the imagination and initiative to make a real difference – to be the difference that matters so much to its clients. It doesn't want clones. Its people are as diverse as its clients: individuals who can think for themselves, appreciate and respect people whoever they are, build relationships and take personal responsibility.

BDO's training is as exceptional – and individual – as the people it recruits. Most study for the ACA, but there are also routes to other professional qualifications. Training is tailored to their needs and centred on first-hand experience. That's why they get such excellent results.

The firm offers successful applicants opportunities in a range of exciting areas from tax to forensic services, with the chance to take real responsibility on projects alongside partners and colleagues. Refreshingly, its partners are known for their hands-on involvement and mutual support is an essential part of the culture. Graduates could also spend time abroad on secondments: BDO is a global accountancy network with more than 1,000 offices in over 100 countries.

BDO has won a number of service and sector related awards including, for the second year in succession, Accountant of the Year at the 2012 M&A Awards and Auditor of the Year at the Real Business' FDs' Excellence Awards 2012.

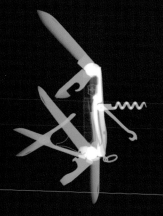

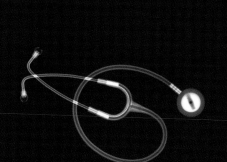

Bloomberg

Bloomberg leads the knowledge economy, delivering the competitive edge through critical information. The firm connects influential decision makers across business, finance and government to a thriving network of news, data, people and ideas.

Bloomberg's clients include corporations, news organisations, financial and legal professionals, and individuals around the world. With over 11,000 employees operating in more than 153 countries, Bloomberg is truly international. The largest offices include New York, London and Tokyo.

Graduate positions include financial analytics and sales, financial software development, global data, news, operations and many more. For most roles, a second language is desirable but not essential. Bloomberg recruits all year round and from any discipline. A passion for finance, technology or an international career is required. Bloomberg breaks down barriers between people and encourages communication by bringing colleagues together. With no job titles or executive areas, the culture fosters interaction at every level. Step into Bloomberg, and graduates will know instantly: it's a different kind of company. From free snacks in the pantry to trending updates on every floor, Bloomberg offer an intersection of speed and collaboration.

Bloomberg supports community programmes by reinvesting resources back into society through sponsorships and employee volunteer activities. However the real depth and diversity of Bloomberg's way of life comes from the creativity and commitment of its people. Training is extensive and ongoing via Bloomberg University. Courses are wide-ranging and available to all, allowing graduates to progress quickly and take on real responsibility fast. Opportunities are listed on the website and start dates are available throughout the year.

GRADUATE VACANCIES IN 2013
FINANCE

IT

MEDIA

SALES

NUMBER OF VACANCIES
300+ graduate jobs

LOCATIONS OF VACANCIES

STARTING SALARY FOR 2013
£Competitive

UNIVERSITY VISITS IN 2012-13
ASTON, BATH, BIRMINGHAM, BRISTOL, CAMBRIDGE, CITY, EDINBURGH, GLASGOW, IMPERIAL COLLEGE LONDON, KING'S COLLEGE LONDON, LEEDS, LIVERPOOL, LONDON SCHOOL OF ECONOMICS, MANCHESTER, NOTTINGHAM, OXFORD, READING, SOUTHAMPTON, UNIVERSITY COLLEGE LONDON, WARWICK, YORK
Please check with your university careers service for full details of local events.

MINIMUM ENTRY REQUIREMENTS
Relevant degree required for some roles.

APPLICATION DEADLINE
Year-round recruitment

FURTHER INFORMATION
www.Top100GraduateEmployers.com
Register now for the latest news, events information and graduate recruitment details for Britain's leading employers.

B

Boots is the UK's leading pharmacy-led health and beauty retailer and one of the country's most trusted household names, with a great heritage and a passion for customers. Following on from the recent announcement of a strategic partnership with Walgreens in the US – the future at Boots looks bright.

Continuing to grow in a tough climate requires a strong team of people who genuinely love driving business performance by creating "feel good" experiences for customers. Graduates play an essential role in this success and join Boots as future business leaders.

The Boots Graduate Programme covers four business areas: The Retail Management Programme; designed to produce future store leaders who can offer Boots' customers the legendary experience they expect each time they walk into a store. The Brand, Buying and Marketing Programme (with an opportunity for an international role) explores how to develop, source and market Boots' brands (including No.7 and Botanics) as well as a huge range of external brands. The Finance Programme offers experience in financial accounting, management information and business partnering. Boots will also fund a relevant financial qualification. The Technology Leadership Programme will develop successful applicants within a highly skilled team whose aim it is to ensure that the company's IT solutions meet the demands of a fast growing business today and in the future.

While a relevant business, retail or finance degree is ideal, it's more important that graduates bring their passion for retail and are excited by the prospect of driving future business. In return they can expect benefits that include great career and development opportunities, generous staff discounts, bonuses based on performance, a stakeholder pension and generous holidays.

GRADUATE VACANCIES IN 2013

FINANCE

IT

MARKETING

PURCHASING

RETAILING

NUMBER OF VACANCIES
45 graduate jobs

LOCATIONS OF VACANCIES

STARTING SALARY FOR 2013
£23,000
Plus excellent benefits.

UNIVERSITY VISITS IN 2012-13
ASTON, MANCHESTER,
NOTTINGHAM, WARWICK
Please check with your university careers service for full details of local events.

APPLICATION DEADLINE
30th November 2012

FURTHER INFORMATION
www.Top100GraduateEmployers.com
Register now for the latest news, events information and graduate recruitment details for Britain's leading employers.

Feel inspired

"The first thing I noticed was the sheer size – and seeing just how many people work behind the scenes was awe-inspiring."

Ravi, Boots Finance Programme

Join us as a graduate in Brand, Buying and Marketing, Retail Management, Finance or Technology Leadership, and you'll feel inspired every day – with real responsibility from day one, incredible support, plus the chance to experience different roles in your chosen field. From there, the opportunities are endless; we're looking for business leaders of the future, all with the UK's leading healthcare and beauty retailer, and one of the Sunday Times' top 25 best big employers.

Find out more about the Boots Graduate Programme
www.boots.jobs/graduates

Boots
feel good

THE SUNDAY TIMES
25
BEST BIG
COMPANIES
TO WORK FOR
2012

Grow Further.

The Boston Consulting Group (BCG) is a global management consulting firm and the world's leading advisor on business strategy. Founded in 1963, the Boston Consulting Group is a private partnership with 75 offices in 42 countries and $3.6B in annual revenues.

BCG partners with clients from all sectors and regions to navigate demanding business environments, identify their highest-value opportunities and transform their businesses. BCG's customised, collaborative approach combines deep insight with close collaboration at all levels of the client organisation. This ensures that its clients achieve competitive advantage, build more capable organisations and secure lasting results. Since 1990, the firm has grown at an industry-beating 15 percent annually. BCG is looking for new graduates or young professionals to continue this success – people as passionate as BCG is about creating lasting change.

As part of a winning team, BCG consultants work daily with the world's leading companies to solve their toughest issues and help leaders in business not just play better, but change the rules of the game. They are inspired, challenged and mentored by the best business minds and grow by gaining unique client experience and exposure.

BCG offers an unmatched platform for personal growth. Its targeted training programme supports the development of a comprehensive toolkit of business, management and interpersonal skills. In addition, BCG sponsors its consultants in MBA studies at leading business schools, supports (social impact) secondments with world-class clients, and provides international work opportunities. The knowledge, experience and skills gained will provide the springboard to excel in any field within BCG or beyond.

Grow Further.

YOUR FUTURE STARTS HERE.

At BCG, your potential is limited only by your talents and ambitions. The knowledge, expertise, and skills you gain will provide the springboard to excel in any field—within BCG and beyond. We grow, you grow with us.

To learn more about BCG, our work, and our people please visit our Web site *www.bcg.london.com*

THE BOSTON CONSULTING GROUP

We employ
more than

80,000
people in

55
countries across

6
continents

Heat. Light. Power. Mobility. Materials for the products that define modern life. All are made possible by oil and gas. Delivering them safely, sustainably and cost effectively is what BP's business is all about. And remains one of the biggest challenges in the world today.

To help the company meet that challenge, BP recruits talented and ambitious graduates at every stage of the energy life cycle – from geoscientists sending shock waves through the earth to find new oil and gas reserves and engineers building platforms in the ocean to extract them, to traders anticipating and reacting to changes in the markets around them.

Whether graduates want to be future business leaders, world-class scientists or ground-breaking engineers, BP's three-year 'Challenge' is designed to help them develop the skills and experience they need to excel. At the same time, it offers a unique insight into the workings of one of the world's leading international oil and gas companies and a chance to discover what an incredible organisation it is to be part of.

Because BP offers such a breadth of opportunity graduates can join them with a good degree in practically any discipline. Wherever a graduate's talent and aspiration lies, a high level of academic achievement is expected. But every bit as important are the individual attributes and personal qualities graduates bring.

Together, BP people are determined to make a positive difference through their work; to create an enduring legacy that benefits the world for generations to come. The company's whole approach is built on teamwork, trust and respect, being consistent and having the courage to do the right thing. All of which is underpinned by a commitment to safety and excellence in all they do. It's essential that their graduates share those values too.

I DISCOVERED MY SEA LEGS
100 MILES WEST OF SHETLAND

My family and friends are still amazed that I work offshore. But there's no way I was going to pass up the chance to spend time out here in the Foinaven field. I suppose my interest in chemical engineering was sparked when I was a kid, watching the news and developments in the Middle East. It demonstrated the crucial role the oil industry has to play in society as a whole, and I knew I wanted to be part of that. Now I've found my feet out here on our floating production, storage and offloading (FPSO) vessel, it's true to say I couldn't be more directly involved.

HANI BALUCH, PETROLEUM ENGINEER, UK

Using down-hole and well-head sensors, we create a virtual image of operating conditions in the field and estimate production well by well.

What will you discover?

At BP, we offer the most exciting and challenging global opportunities for high performing graduates in engineering, science and business.

bp.com/ukgraduates/hani

bp

British Airways is the UK's largest international airline. They fly more than 32 million customers to 145 destinations worldwide every single year. Making this happen involves the drive and dedication of some 43,000 people, from cargo agents, financial experts and IT specialists, through to cabin crew, pilots, and of course, more than a few talented graduates.

It's not just customers that British Airways helps get to where they want to go. The fact is they can do the same for graduates too, with a range of first class professional development programmes including Leaders For Business, Operational Research, HR, IT, Engineering, World Cargo, Finance and Procurement.

No matter which of the programmes fuels graduates' passion most, BA can provide them with the opportunities they're looking for and help them develop a career that lets them be inspired, innovative and outstanding, all at once. Think real roles with real responsibilities. Exposure to different business areas and major projects. Involvement in key business decisions. The unique chance to make an impact on an international scale. And of course, the opportunity to gain relevant qualifications such as CIMA, CIPS or ACCA.

Those who are outstanding really do stand out. That's why successful applicants will need excellent academics to be successful. They will also need to have the right to live and work in the UK, along with the right attitude and the drive to go above and beyond excellent all the time, every time.

With the exception of IT, where graduates will be based at either London or Newcastle, the rest of BA's programmes are initially based in London, but it might also be necessary to move to other locations.

GRADUATE VACANCIES IN 2013

CONSULTING
ENGINEERING
FINANCE
GENERAL MANAGEMENT
HUMAN RESOURCES
IT
LOGISTICS
PURCHASING
RESEARCH & DEVELOPMENT

NUMBER OF VACANCIES
Up to 70 graduate jobs

LOCATIONS OF VACANCIES

STARTING SALARY FOR 2013
£24,000

UNIVERSITY VISITS IN 2012-13
Please check with your university careers service for full details of local events.

MINIMUM ENTRY REQUIREMENTS
2.1 Degree

APPLICATION DEADLINE
Please see website for full details.

FURTHER INFORMATION
www.Top100GraduateEmployers.com
Register now for the latest news, events information and graduate recruitment details for Britain's leading employers.

BRITISH AIRWAYS

We're painting brighter futures.
Especially for those of you
who want to be outstanding.

Graduate Careers. Be outstanding.

BRITISH SUGAR

An **AB Sugar** Company

EXCEEDING **YOUR** *expectations*

British Sugar is the UK's leading sugar supplier to food and drink manufacturers in the UK and Europe, and with around 4,000 growers supplying its four factories the business produces over 1 million tonnes of sugar. Beyond sugar production there is a surprisingly diverse business to be discovered.

Although sugar remains at the core of its operations, by using a highly integrated approach to manufacturing, they aim to transform all raw materials into sustainable products, from tomatoes to animal feed, making it a truly diverse and exciting business to work for.

With such a fast moving industry the British Sugar graduate scheme is not an average scheme. Graduates can expect a high degree of challenges throughout their career with no two days ever the same.

Successful graduates are at the heart of British Sugars talent pool and will stand out for their passion, drive, adaptability, a desire to challenge and a can-do attitude. In return graduates can expect immediate responsibility, support throughout the scheme, and to be equipped with a wealth of knowledge and experience to become leaders of the future.

British Sugar offers a range of development programmes for the following disciplines: Engineering, Science, Agriculture, Business and Procurement and Finance. All programmes are equally challenging, and graduates will build a unique portfolio of skills by rotating around teams and/or factories to gain an understanding of the business and the way in which British Sugar operates.

Candidates should visit the graduate website for more information on the scheme and the different disciplines on offer.

British Sugar is part of AB Sugar, which is wholly owned by international food, ingredients and retail group, Associated British Foods plc.

GRADUATE VACANCIES IN 2013
ACCOUNTANCY
ENGINEERING
FINANCE
GENERAL MANAGEMENT
LOGISTICS
PURCHASING
SALES

NUMBER OF VACANCIES
14 graduate jobs

LOCATIONS OF VACANCIES

STARTING SALARY FOR 2013
£25,000-£30,000
Plus a £1,500 joining bonus.

UNIVERSITY VISITS IN 2012-13
BATH, BIRMINGHAM, CAMBRIDGE,
DURHAM, EDINBURGH, LEEDS,
LOUGHBOROUGH, MANCHESTER,
NEWCASTLE, NOTTINGHAM, READING,
SHEFFIELD, STRATHCLYDE, WARWICK
Please check with your university careers service for full details of local events.

MINIMUM ENTRY REQUIREMENTS
2.1 Degree

APPLICATION DEADLINE
31st January 2013

FURTHER INFORMATION
www.Top100GraduateEmployers.com
Register now for the latest news, events information and graduate recruitment details for Britain's leading employers.

BT

www.btgraduates.com

twitter.com/btgradcareers facebook.com/BTGraduateCareers

Welcome to a world of innovation. With over 600 patents registered in the past five years, BT are one of the world's leading providers of innovative IT and communication services. They're always looking for new ways to help businesses and people become more connected, more productive and more competitive.

But staying ahead in the industry isn't just about technology. It's about people too. People who want to challenge the norm, think of new and better ways to do things and work as part of a team to make them happen. Diversity is at the very heart of the company. In order to provide the very best products and services to their varied customer base they need a diverse workforce to imagine, create and deliver the solutions required both now and into the future. This means creating a working environment that includes and recognises such diversity.

So what makes a successful BT graduate? Leadership potential? Teamworking ability? Creativity? Enthusiasm? Or communication skills? BT looks for all of these qualities. And more. They look for people who don't wait to be told what to do, and who can't wait to get involved.

BT graduates work on real projects, with real responsibility from the start. Whatever they're involved in – whether it's technology, business management, marketing, sales, HR, or legal – they're encouraged to take the initiative.

It's about taking talent and developing future leaders. Throughout the programme, graduates benefit from ongoing training, both on the job and in the classroom. From talent master classes, through to leadership development and commercial awareness as well as professional development, every opportunity is there to be seized. There's huge scope for graduates to shape their own career. To make the most of their leadership potential. And to get connected to the big wide world of BT.

GRADUATE VACANCIES IN 2013

CONSULTING
ENGINEERING
GENERAL MANAGEMENT
HUMAN RESOURCES
IT
LAW
MARKETING
RESEARCH & DEVELOPMENT
SALES

NUMBER OF VACANCIES
Around 200 graduate jobs

LOCATIONS OF VACANCIES

STARTING SALARY FOR 2013
£27,500-£31,500

UNIVERSITY VISITS IN 2012-13
ASTON, BATH, BELFAST, BIRMINGHAM, BRISTOL, CAMBRIDGE, CITY, DURHAM, EDINBURGH, ESSEX, GLASGOW, IMPERIAL COLLEGE LONDON, KING'S COLLEGE LONDON, LANCASTER, LEEDS, LOUGHBOROUGH, MANCHESTER, NOTTINGHAM, OXFORD, SHEFFIELD, SOUTHAMPTON, STRATHCLYDE, WARWICK, YORK
Please check with your university careers service for full details of local events.

MINIMUM ENTRY REQUIREMENTS
2.1 Degree
320 UCAS points
280 points for Technology.
Relevant degree required for some roles.

APPLICATION DEADLINE
Varies by function

FURTHER INFORMATION
www.Top100GraduateEmployers.com
Register now for the latest news, events information and graduate recruitment details for Britain's leading employers.

Get connected...

...to the best graduate opportunities

With over 600 patents registered in the past five years, BT are one of the world's leading providers of innovative IT and communication services. Known globally as a major technology player – pioneering digital advances that will shape the future.

BT has graduate opportunities in:
- Technology
- Business Management
- Marketing
- Sales
- HR
- Legal

Get connected to the big wide world of BT.
Visit **www.btgraduates.com**

Cancer Research UK is a life-saving organisation. Its pioneering research delivers the breakthroughs which prevent, control and cure cancer. They combine cutting-edge science, business expertise and marketing talent, making it a world class centre of scientific excellence and the largest fundraising charity in the UK.

Every year, Cancer Research UK offers a variety of graduate opportunities in all aspects of their work, including fundraising, marketing, communications, science and corporate services. Few organisations can offer such a unique range of opportunities or allow graduates to make a real contribution. As well as graduate programmes, Cancer Research UK offers PhD studentships, internships, industrial placements and a variety of voluntary opportunities.

Driven by a single cause – to bring forward the day when all cancers are cured – every member of staff has a fundamental role to play. Clearly, a career with Cancer Research UK offers plenty in the way of personal fulfilment, but it's also a considerable challenge, calling for innovative, brave and smart individuals. Cancer Research UK is ambitious and driven to succeed, and needs the right people to help achieve their vision. Successful candidates will demonstrate excellent communication skills, a willingness to go the extra mile to achieve exceptional results, and the ability to build strong relationships. Most importantly they'll share the organisation's passion for the vital work it does.

To help successful applicants achieve their ambitions, graduates will benefit from a unique combination of on-the-job learning and formal training. Whichever way is best, graduates will have all the support they need from peers, managers and a mentor to help shape future growth.

Cancer Research UK offers outstanding graduates the opportunity to work towards an outstanding vision.

GRADUATE VACANCIES IN 2013
FINANCE
GENERAL MANAGEMENT
HUMAN RESOURCES
IT
MARKETING
RESEARCH & DEVELOPMENT
RETAILING

NUMBER OF VACANCIES
Around 100 graduate jobs

LOCATIONS OF VACANCIES

STARTING SALARY FOR 2013
£Competitive

UNIVERSITY VISITS IN 2012-13
BATH, BRISTOL, LOUGHBOROUGH, NOTTINGHAM, OXFORD, SOUTHAMPTON, WARWICK
Please check with your university careers service for full details of local events.

MINIMUM ENTRY REQUIREMENTS
2.1 Degree

APPLICATION DEADLINE
January 2013

FURTHER INFORMATION
www.Top100GraduateEmployers.com
Register now for the latest news, events information and graduate recruitment details for Britain's leading employers.

USE YOUR HEAD

CHOOSE A GRADUATE EMPLOYER THAT'S IN THE TIMES TOP 100

FOLLOW YOUR HEART

BE PART OF AN ORGANISATION THAT'S LEADING THE FIGHT AGAINST CANCER

GRADUATE OPPORTUNITIES.

Cancer Research UK is an inspiring story about smart, brave people who came together to beat cancer. Over the last century, we've built an international reputation for excellence. So, when you join us as a graduate, you won't just benefit from training and development that's earned us a place in the Times Top 100. You'll be following in the footsteps of the industry's biggest talents – and shaping the growth of the world's leading cancer charity dedicated to saving lives.

Find out more at graduates.cancerresearchuk.org

CANCER
RESEARCH
UK

centrica

Centrica is an international energy company that sources, generates, processes, stores, trades, supplies, services and helps its customers save energy. Securing energy to power the future is an important priority for everyone who works at Centrica, and the company is making vital investments across the entire energy spectrum.

As a top 30 FTSE 100 company with over 25 million customer accounts, a £22 billion turnover and more than 34,000 employees, Centrica is the parent company for a range of global brands. British Gas and Direct Energy supply power and related services in the UK and North America respectively; Direct Energy and Centrica Energy in the UK manage power generation, gas and oil production and trading operations to ensure day-to-day demand is met, and Centrica Storage is the largest gas storage facility in the UK.

Graduates could be getting involved in any area of the energy lifecycle – from exploration and production with Centrica Energy, to front-line customer service management at British Gas – although the exact role will depend on which of the schemes they join. The graduate programme has been designed to offer a broad grounding in the business; those who are ambitious and commercially savvy have an outstanding opportunity to be a future business leader in this diverse organisation.

Developing graduates is important to Centrica; graduate talent boards ensure they have the opportunity to fulfil their potential and are equipped with the right skills and behaviours to help grow the business and implement Centrica's strategy. It all adds up to an award-winning programme that offers graduates who are up for big challenges the opportunity to get involved in a variety of areas – as well as receiving support and reward along the way.

GRADUATE VACANCIES IN 2013
ENGINEERING
FINANCE
GENERAL MANAGEMENT
HUMAN RESOURCES
IT
MARKETING

NUMBER OF VACANCIES
60+ graduate jobs

LOCATIONS OF VACANCIES

STARTING SALARY FOR 2013
£Competitive

UNIVERSITY VISITS IN 2012-13
CAMBRIDGE, DURHAM, IMPERIAL COLLEGE LONDON, LANCASTER, LOUGHBOROUGH, MANCHESTER, NOTTINGHAM, OXFORD, SHEFFIELD, SOUTHAMPTON, STRATHCLYDE, WARWICK
Please check with your university careers service for full details of local events.

MINIMUM ENTRY REQUIREMENTS
Relevant degree required for some roles.

APPLICATION DEADLINE
Please see website for full details.

FURTHER INFORMATION
www.Top100GraduateEmployers.com
Register now for the latest news, events information and graduate recruitment details for Britain's leading employers.

Graduate & Summer Placement
Opportunities

We source it

We generate it

We process it

We store it

Where could
you fit in?

We trade it

We supply it

We service it

We save it

Centrica is the UK's leading energy supplier and one of the greenest – sourcing, generating, processing, storing, trading, supplying, servicing and saving energy for some 25 million customer accounts.

Help us shape the future of energy and we'll help you to flourish. Graduate opportunities exist in **Customer Operations; Marketing; Human Resources; Analyst; Information Systems; Finance; Engineering Subsurface; and Health, Safety & Environment.** We also run a 10-week **Summer Placement Programme.**

Find out more by visiting our website.
www.centrica.com/Graduates

Since Citi opened its first office in New York in 1812, it has answered the needs of economies, businesses and communities in hundreds of cities, in over 160 countries, thriving in the most challenging times over a 200 year history. Citi's global presence isn't just a question of size, it's a way of thinking.

A career with Citi means being part of a global firm that provides the most forward-thinking financial products and solutions to the most enterprising corporations, institutions, governments and individuals around the world.

Citi's success is driven by its exceptional people – their passion, dedication and entrepreneurship – and it will be graduates who will shape its future. At Citi, learning doesn't stop at graduation and there are many ways to embark on a rewarding career path, enjoying the global opportunities and long-term training and development initiatives experienced by over 260,000 employees worldwide.

Citi offers full-time and internship opportunities across a number of its business areas, including Investment Banking, Corporate Banking, Capital Markets Origination, Sales & Trading, Citi Transaction Services, Private Bank, Risk Management, Human Resources and Operations & Technology. Citi also offers insight programmes enabling students in their first year (or in their second year of a four year course) to experience firsthand the Citi culture and environment. Graduates interested in this industry with drive, commitment and a passion for learning are encouraged to apply.

This is the opportunity to be part of an exciting period in the development of the global financial services industry, working with the brightest minds to drive responsible, positive change across the organisation, the banking industry, and beyond.

GRADUATE VACANCIES IN 2013

FINANCE

HUMAN RESOURCES

INVESTMENT BANKING

IT

NUMBER OF VACANCIES
250+ graduate jobs

LOCATIONS OF VACANCIES

STARTING SALARY FOR 2013
£Competitive
Relocation allowance, private healthcare, life assurance and pension scheme (with company contribution).

UNIVERSITY VISITS IN 2012-13
BATH, BELFAST, BRISTOL, CAMBRIDGE, DURHAM, EDINBURGH, IMPERIAL COLLEGE LONDON, KING'S COLLEGE LONDON, LONDON SCHOOL OF ECONOMICS, MANCHESTER, NOTTINGHAM, OXFORD, ST ANDREWS, UNIVERSITY COLLEGE LONDON, WARWICK
Please check with your university careers service for full details of local events.

MINIMUM ENTRY REQUIREMENTS
2.1 Degree

APPLICATION DEADLINE
Varies by function
Early application advised. Please see website for full details.

FURTHER INFORMATION
www.Top100GraduateEmployers.com
Register now for the latest news, events information and graduate recruitment details for Britain's leading employers.

your place is here

Career opportunities with Citi

Here is where you have an idea. Which inspires change. Making a difference to economies, businesses and communities all over the world. That's the beauty of here: it's where future thinking happens every day.

your place is here

Education. Health. Justice. Employment. Defence. Transport. Climate change. International development and foreign affairs. These are just some of the areas where graduates on the Civil Service Fast Stream get to put their ideas into practice, as they work on issues that affect the entire country and beyond.

The Civil Service Fast Stream is an accelerated training and development programme for graduates with the potential to become the future leaders of the Civil Service. As such, Fast Streamers are given considerable early responsibility from the outset, they are stretched and challenged on a daily basis, and they move regularly between projects to gain a wide range of experiences and skills.

They experience work in a range of professional areas: operational delivery, policy development, corporate services, people management, commercial awareness, financial management and/or project and programme management. These areas give them a wide understanding of how government delivers public services. A comprehensive training and development programme combined with on-the-job learning is provided to support achievement of the Fast Stream role.

So what qualities are needed to make it to the top? Initiative, confidence, innovation, orally articulate, strong drafting skills, leadership and self awareness. Above all, they need to be the kind of people who can build constructive relationships and deliver results, and who are excited by the idea of making a positive and highly visible impact across many different areas of society.

There are opportunities available across the UK in all areas of government, which offer graduates a unique perspective of work at the heart of current affairs and key government agendas. There's no limit to where their ideas could end up on the Civil Service Fast Stream. All degree disciplines are welcome.

GRADUATE VACANCIES IN 2013
ENGINEERING
GENERAL MANAGEMENT
HUMAN RESOURCES
IT

NUMBER OF VACANCIES
300-400 graduate jobs

LOCATIONS OF VACANCIES

STARTING SALARY FOR 2013
£25,000-£27,000

UNIVERSITY VISITS IN 2012-13
Please check with your university careers service for full details of local events.

MINIMUM ENTRY REQUIREMENTS
2.2 Degree

APPLICATION DEADLINE
30th November 2012

FURTHER INFORMATION
www.Top100GraduateEmployers.com
Register now for the latest news, events information and graduate recruitment details for Britain's leading employers.

where will your IDEAS end up?

CIVILSERVICE
FASTSTREAM

CLIFFORD CHANCE

Clifford Chance's goal is to be at the forefront of the elite group of international law firms. Joining the firm requires an appreciation of the commercial context in which they offer advice and a willingness to help businesses and individuals address the challenges of succeeding in increasingly complex and global markets.

Clifford Chance advises multi-national and domestic corporates, financial institutions, regulatory authorities, supranational bodies, governments and government agencies. The firm works internationally and domestically; on day-to-day operations and on 'game-changing' transformational deals and issues.

Clifford Chance is regularly singled out for the quality of its client service and legal expertise. Recent accolades include: International Law Firm of the Year for Europe (IFLR Europe Awards 2012), the Middle East (Corporate Counsel Awards 2012) and Asia Pacific (Chambers Asia Pacific Awards 2012), and more tier-one rankings in the global tables of Chambers Global 2012 than any other firm.

Clifford Chance is a firm of exceptional lawyers drawn from a wide range of backgrounds – there is no one 'type'. Instead the firm aims to recruit people who can help give their clients a competitive edge in challenging situations. They are interested in people who have the potential to become outstanding lawyers – regardless of what they have studied at university.

Clifford Chance ask a lot of their trainees. Focus and dedication are essential, but they will also need to be flexible and willing to adapt to new challenges and a lot of responsibility. Counterbalancing this is a level of investment in career development and a level of international opportunity that is only offered by a handful of professional services firms.

GRADUATE VACANCIES IN 2013

LAW

NUMBER OF VACANCIES
100 graduate jobs
For training contracts starting in 2015.

LOCATIONS OF VACANCIES

STARTING SALARY FOR 2013
£38,000

UNIVERSITY VISITS IN 2012-13
ABERDEEN, BIRMINGHAM, BRISTOL, CAMBRIDGE, DUNDEE, DURHAM, EXETER, GLASGOW, KING'S COLLEGE LONDON, LEICESTER, LONDON SCHOOL OF ECONOMICS, MANCHESTER, NEWCASTLE, NOTTINGHAM, OXFORD, QUEEN MARY LONDON, READING, SHEFFIELD, SCHOOL OF AFRICAN STUDIES, SOUTHAMPTON, ST ANDREWS, UNIVERSITY COLLEGE LONDON, WARWICK, YORK
Please check with your university careers service for full details of local events.

MINIMUM ENTRY REQUIREMENTS
2.1 Degree
340 UCAS points

APPLICATION DEADLINE
Law: 31st July 2013
Non-law: 1st January 2013

FURTHER INFORMATION
www.Top100GraduateEmployers.com
Register now for the latest news, events information and graduate recruitment details for Britain's leading employers.

DIVERSE, INTERNATIONAL AND COMMERCIALLY AWARE, WE WORK TOGETHER.

TOGETHER WE ARE CLIFFORD CHANCE.

Joining us as a trainee means sharing our ambition and drive to set the pace among the global elite law firms. You will develop your potential as part of an exceptionally talented legal team, and tackle the issues and decisions that shape our clients' success – helping them to achieve competitive advantage in challenging business circumstances.

Find out about opportunities at Clifford Chance – a law firm built on collaboration, innovation and a relentless commitment to quality, and with more leading cross-border practices than any other firm *(Chambers Global 2012)*.

PIONEER

As the UK's largest co-operative business, The Co-operative Group is co-owned by close to six million members. With an annual turnover of around £13bn, The Group employs more than 110,000 people. Founded on pioneering ethical values, like any business they want to make a healthy profit, but the way they do it is just as important.

The organisation combines ambitious commercial targets with groundbreaking social and sustainable goals. With 15 different businesses and around 5,000 outlets, The Co-operative Group isn't just a food retailer. It's also a travel agency, a funeral director, a pharmacist, a legal services provider, and much more.

So there's plenty for graduates to look forward to, not least the career options on offer. On all of the programmes, graduates will get right to the heart of the commercial approach to business, with the sort of training and development most graduates can only dream of.

So, they're looking for ambitious graduates who want to pursue a successful career without compromising their values. In particular, they want sharp commercial thinkers who bring a pioneering approach to everything they do.

There are five programmes on offer: Business Management, CIMA Finance, Retail, HR and IT. Whichever route graduates take, they'll get the chance to work on a wide range of projects across a family of diverse businesses. They'll also get to see that how they do business, is just as important as what they do.

On all the programmes, graduates will gain the experience they need, and develop technical knowledge and professional skills through a comprehensive development programme, a buddy, a personal development budget, a structured training programme and a mentor from within The Group.

LOCATIONS OF VACANCIES

STARTING SALARY FOR 2013
£24,000
Plus a £2,000 discretional bonus at the end of the first year.

UNIVERSITY VISITS IN 2012-13
CAMBRIDGE, DURHAM, LANCASTER, LEEDS, LIVERPOOL, MANCHESTER, NOTTINGHAM, SHEFFIELD
Please check with your university careers service for full details of local events.

MINIMUM ENTRY REQUIREMENTS
2.2 Degree

APPLICATION DEADLINE
31st December 2012

FURTHER INFORMATION
www.Top100GraduateEmployers.com
Register now for the latest news, events information and graduate recruitment details for Britain's leading employers.

The **co-operative**
good for everyone

FROM SUPPORTING
FAIRTRADE TO
BOOSTING **UK TRADE.**

What will you pioneer?

As a **graduate** at The Co-operative, you'll be part of a culture that combines sharp commercial thinking with an ethical conscience. So you won't just be working in a business that pioneered Fairtrade products in the UK. You'll be based in the heart of Manchester, the centre of a huge regeneration project that's set to boost the UK economy and transform the local landscape of the city. Good news for your future. And the future of everyone around you.

BECOME A PIONEER: CO-OPERATIVE.JOBS/GRADUATES
Finance | Business Management | Retail | HR | IT

Credit Suisse is a forward-thinking financial services firm serving clients around the globe. As a stable company with a long banking tradition, it is one of the most respected banks in the world. Indeed, the firm is a leading player in many key markets – recognised by industry publications for its continued excellence.

At Credit Suisse graduates are given the chance to make a difference from day one, and are provided world-class training and support to help develop them into a future business leader. In addition to on-the-job experience, they receive formal training and mentoring tailored to their needs and to the demands of their chosen business area. This is the first step in a programme of continuous professional development that will be offered throughout their career.

Summer internships typically last for ten weeks and are one of the most in-depth programmes in the financial services industry. They offer intellectual challenges and real business experience where one gains meaningful insight into the different areas of the business. Interns face real challenges, enjoy real achievements, and have their talents recognised every step of the way. Interns receive world class classroom training and on-the-job experience, and above all, will develop a skill set that will set them apart.

Credit Suisse's vision is to become the world's most admired bank. It looks for people with a wide range of experiences, interests and degrees who will add fresh perspectives to its business. A career with the firm offers the chance to shape its future.

Opportunities are available in the Investment Banking Department, Fixed Income, Equities, Asset Management, Information Technology, Investment Banking Operations and Finance.

GRADUATE VACANCIES IN 2013

FINANCE

INVESTMENT BANKING

IT

NUMBER OF VACANCIES
275 graduate jobs

LOCATIONS OF VACANCIES

STARTING SALARY FOR 2013
£Competitive

UNIVERSITY VISITS IN 2012-13
BIRMINGHAM, CAMBRIDGE, IMPERIAL COLLEGE LONDON, KING'S COLLEGE LONDON, LONDON SCHOOL OF ECONOMICS, MANCHESTER, OXFORD, SOUTHAMPTON, UNIVERSITY COLLEGE LONDON, WARWICK
Please check with your university careers service for full details of local events.

MINIMUM ENTRY REQUIREMENTS
2.1 Degree

APPLICATION DEADLINE
18th November 2012

FURTHER INFORMATION
www.Top100GraduateEmployers.com
Register now for the latest news, events information and graduate recruitment details for Britain's leading employers.

CREDIT SUISSE

Credit Suisse Careers
Student Program Application Deadlines

Opportunities are available in the Investment Banking Department, Fixed Income, Equities, Asset Management, Information Technology, Global Operations and Finance.

Our Summer Internships are one of the most in-depth 10 week programs in the financial services industry. **Apply by: 16 December 2012**

Our Spring Program is a five day introduction to the investment banking industry. Apply by: 02 January 2013

**To find out more and apply online
visit credit-suisse.com/careers**

Deloitte.

It's your future.
How far will you take it?

GRADUATE VACANCIES IN 2013

ACCOUNTANCY

CONSULTING

FINANCE

IT

PROPERTY

NUMBER OF VACANCIES
1,200 graduate jobs

LOCATIONS OF VACANCIES

Helping the biggest businesses make some of their biggest decisions. Tackling the most complex operations. Leading the leading-edge. Developing expertise not just in one company, but in entire industries. This is what it means to be a professional at Deloitte, the world's largest professional services firm – whether that's in Audit, Tax, Consulting, Corporate Finance or Technology.

In fact, Deloitte works with some of the greatest names in the world of business – and employ some of the foremost experts in their fields. New graduates will be joining their ranks, working alongside them and exploring the intricacies of a variety of clients' organisations.

The work itself gives graduates an unparalleled start to their career in business. They will tackle a wide range of assignments with high-profile clients across different sectors; receive coaching from senior colleagues; benefit from world-class training and development; and have the opportunity to study for professional qualifications. What's more, the rewards on offer are some of the best in the industry, and graduates will be encouraged along with their colleagues to donate their time and energy to worthwhile projects in the community.

All of this leads to a bright future for the graduates who join Deloitte, allowing them to build up wide-ranging business networks, and gain exposure on the kind of projects and clients that any business professional would be proud of.

Deloitte has a variety of graduate and undergraduate opportunities available across all of their service lines, and in many different regions throughout the country. They welcome people of every background and any degree discipline. Opportunities are offered on a first come first serve basis, so it is worth getting applications in early.

STARTING SALARY FOR 2013
£Competitive
Plus a mix of core and optional benefits.

UNIVERSITY VISITS IN 2012-13
ABERDEEN, ASTON, BATH, BELFAST, BIRMINGHAM, BRISTOL, CAMBRIDGE, CARDIFF, CITY, DUNDEE, DURHAM, EDINBURGH, EXETER, GLASGOW, HERIOT-WATT, IMPERIAL COLLEGE LONDON, KING'S COLLEGE LONDON, KENT, LANCASTER, LEEDS, LEICESTER, LIVERPOOL, LONDON SCHOOL OF ECONOMICS, LOUGHBOROUGH, MANCHESTER, NEWCASTLE, NORTHUMBRIA, NOTTINGHAM, NOTTINGHAM TRENT, OXFORD, OXFORD BROOKES, QUEEN MARY LONDON, READING, ROYAL HOLLOWAY LONDON, SHEFFIELD, SOUTHAMPTON, ST ANDREWS, STRATHCLYDE, SURREY, SWANSEA, TRINITY COLLEGE DUBLIN, ULSTER, UNIVERSITY COLLEGE DUBLIN, UNIVERSITY COLLEGE LONDON, WARWICK, YORK
Please check with your university careers service for full details of local events.

MINIMUM ENTRY REQUIREMENTS
2.1 Degree
300 UCAS points

APPLICATION DEADLINE
Year-round recruitment
Early application advised.

FURTHER INFORMATION
www.Top100GraduateEmployers.com
Register now for the latest news, events information and graduate recruitment details for Britain's leading employers.

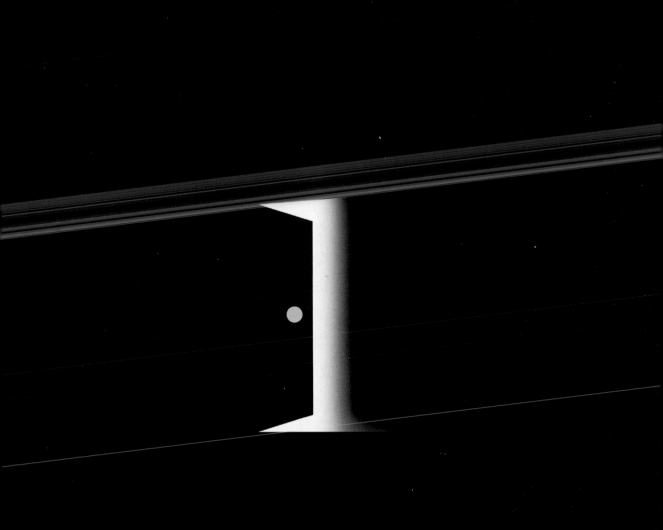

Step into the best career in business

An extraordinary future in business opens up when you join Deloitte. Few will be able to match the network you'll build, the exposure you'll gain and the expertise you'll develop with us. In fact, we'll give you all you need to become someone the world's biggest businesses turn to for advice. It's your future. How far will you take it?

www.deloitte.co.uk/TT100

 youtube.com/
deloitte

 linkedin.com/
company/deloitte-uk

 twitter.com/
DeloitteJobsUK

 facebook.com/
yourfutureatdeloitteuk

Deloitte.

Department
for International
Development

© Lindsay Mgbor/DFID

The Department for International Development (DFID) leads the UK Government's fight against world poverty. Since its creation, DFID has helped more than 250 million people lift themselves from poverty and helped 40 million more children to go to primary school. But there is still much to do.

DFID works with national and international partners to eliminate global poverty and its causes, as part of the UN 'Millennium Development Goals'. It also responds to overseas emergencies.

DFID's Graduate Development Scheme offers a diverse range of work experience in key teams across DFID, all united by a single goal: to tackle poverty and help people in developing countries improve their lives.

During the paid 50 week development placement, successful applicants will work with experienced professionals on specific projects, for example, contributing to evaluating where, when and how DFID delivers the UK's aid programme. They will take on a role suited to their skills, experience and career aims, in one of a number of areas, including: research and evaluation; Africa policy and development; conflict, humanitarian crisis and security; European Union policy; United Nations and Commonwealth policy; youth development and policy; health; Finance, H.R. and I.T.

DFID is committed to supporting all staff to realise their potential. When graduates join DFID, they will have a structured development programme designed to help them learn and contribute as quickly as possible. Their personal development plan will include training and prominent speaker events, e-learning, a mentor and dedicated time for reflection and peer-to-peer learning.

DFID is an equal opportunities employer, welcoming applications from all parts of the community.

GRADUATE VACANCIES IN 2013

ENGINEERING
FINANCE
GENERAL MANAGEMENT
HUMAN RESOURCES
IT
PURCHASING
RESEARCH & DEVELOPMENT

NUMBER OF VACANCIES
50 graduate jobs

LOCATIONS OF VACANCIES

STARTING SALARY FOR 2013
£22,000

UNIVERSITY VISITS IN 2012-13
Please check with your university careers service for full details of local events.

MINIMUM ENTRY REQUIREMENTS
2.1 Degree

APPLICATION DEADLINE
12th March 2013

FURTHER INFORMATION
www.Top100GraduateEmployers.com
Register now for the latest news, events information and graduate recruitment details for Britain's leading employers.

© Brian Sokol

Department for International Development
Graduate Development Opportunities

Department
for International
Development

ukaid
from the British people

The Department for International Development (DFID) leads Britain's fight against global poverty, delivering UK aid around the world.

DFID works with national and international partners from two UK headquarters in London and Glasgow (East Kilbride) and through our network of offices throughout the world.

Our Graduate Development Scheme offers a diverse range of work experience opportunities in key teams across DFID, all united by a single goal: to tackle poverty and help people in developing countries improve their lives.

What could be more worthwhile than that?

Apply online at

www.dfid.gov.uk/graduate

To be eligible for the DFID Graduate Development Scheme you must meet our academic and nationality requirements. Details of these are available on the website.

DIAGEO

While they may not know the company, people everywhere have heard of the brands; Smirnoff, Baileys, Guinness and Johnnie Walker are among the world's best loved. And graduates who'd relish the chance to join the talented team behind them should get in touch with... Guess Who?

Diageo. The world's leading premium drinks business with an outstanding collection of beverage alcohol brands across spirits, beer and wine. Diageo employs over 23,000 people in 80 countries. All with one aim: to help millions of people celebrate life every day, everywhere.

Diageo celebrates success. Through its unique culture involving close collaboration and true team spirit, the company prides itself on achieving things that others may consider unachievable.

Successful applicants to Diageo's structured, three-year programmes will be bright, curious and passionate graduates. Some will have an entrepreneurial spirit for Sales or a creative flair for Consumer Marketing. Others will find their niche in Human Resources, Manufacturing or Supply Chain. All will be provided with outstanding training and real challenges from day one – preparing them to become future leaders, with support from a dedicated buddy and mentor. Being a truly global company, Diageo also offers opportunities to work in different parts of the world.

Diageo looks for people who are authentic in what they do; people who can demonstrate high levels of integrity. Being able to generate new ideas, see them through to action and consistently deliver great performance is essential.

As expected, Diageo offers a competitive salary, a happy work/life balance and great benefits to help its graduates live life to the full. No wonder it's among the world's most admired companies to work for.

GRADUATE VACANCIES IN 2013
ENGINEERING
HUMAN RESOURCES
MARKETING
SALES

NUMBER OF VACANCIES
50 graduate jobs

LOCATIONS OF VACANCIES

Vacancies also available in Europe.

STARTING SALARY FOR 2013
£Competitive

UNIVERSITY VISITS IN 2012-13
BATH, BELFAST, DURHAM, EDINBURGH, EXETER, LANCASTER, LEEDS, LOUGHBOROUGH, NEWCASTLE, NOTTINGHAM, OXFORD, STRATHCLYDE, TRINITY COLLEGE DUBLIN, UNIVERSITY COLLEGE DUBLIN, WARWICK
Please check with your university careers service for full details of local events.

MINIMUM ENTRY REQUIREMENTS
2.1 Degree
300 UCAS points

APPLICATION DEADLINE
Year-round recruitment
Early application advised.

FURTHER INFORMATION
www.Top100GraduateEmployers.com
Register now for the latest news, events information and graduate recruitment details for Britain's leading employers.

Guinness, José Cuervo, Pimm's, Baileys, Johnnie Walker, Smirnoff,... how long did it take you to recognise our brands? Probably not that long. After all, they're some of the best known in the world. The real question, though, is do you know the name behind them all? The answer is Diageo. We're the world's leading premium drinks company – and we're looking for bright graduates who'd like the chance to work on some of the world's most loved brands. Sounds like you? Discover more at **www.diageo.com/careers**

DIAGEO

GRADUATE VACANCIES IN 2013

LAW

NUMBER OF VACANCIES
90 graduate jobs
For training contracts starting in 2015.

LOCATIONS OF VACANCIES

STARTING SALARY FOR 2013
£22,000-£37,000

UNIVERSITY VISITS IN 2012-13
ABERDEEN, BELFAST, BIRMINGHAM,
BRISTOL, CAMBRIDGE, CITY, DUNDEE,
DURHAM, EDINBURGH, EXETER, GLASGOW,
KING'S COLLEGE LONDON, KENT,
LANCASTER, LEEDS, LEICESTER, LIVERPOOL,
LONDON SCHOOL OF ECONOMICS,
MANCHESTER, NEWCASTLE, NOTTINGHAM,
OXFORD, QUEEN MARY LONDON, SCHOOL
OF AFRICAN STUDIES, SHEFFIELD,
STRATHCLYDE, UNIVERSITY COLLEGE
LONDON, WARWICK, YORK
*Please check with your university careers
service for full details of local events.*

MINIMUM ENTRY REQUIREMENTS
2.1 Degree
320 UCAS points

APPLICATION DEADLINE
31st July 2013

FURTHER INFORMATION
www.Top100GraduateEmployers.com
*Register now for the latest news, events
information and graduate recruitment
details for Britain's leading employers.*

DLA Piper is one of the world's largest law firms, supporting clients with their legal and business needs. Working across more than 30 countries in the Americas, Asia Pacific, Europe, and the Middle East, their vision is to be the leading global business law firm.

DLA Piper practises eight main areas of law; corporate; employment, pensions and benefits; finance and projects; intellectual property and technology; litigation and regulatory; real estate; restructuring; and tax. Their clients include household name companies, financial institutions, FTSE and Fortune 500 enterprises, public bodies and governments. This means that their lawyers work on a variety of cutting-edge and high profile deals and matters.

Their success depends on their people, which is why they place a real emphasis and importance on the trainee recruitment process. The firm has been awarded a commendation for its diversity initiatives and policies, proving a commitment to recruiting and developing people from a wide variety of backgrounds.

DLA Piper welcomes applications from students from all degree disciplines, who have demonstrated consistent academic excellence. In addition they seek ambitious and committed individuals, whose good communication and analytical skills enable them to deal with the intellectual challenges of the job. In return they will offer real responsibility and development, as well as the opportunity to work closely with people at all levels of business and options for international and client secondments.

The firm operates a formal summer scheme, which runs between June and August each year. There are approximately 150 places available around the United Kingdom.

SQUEEZE MORE INTO TWO YEARS
WE OFFER YOU ONE OF THE SHARPEST TRAINING CONTRACTS AROUND

Everything matters and every day counts when you're a trainee at DLA Piper. We squeeze huge amounts of experience, responsibility and personal development into your 24 months with us. That means you get to know more about the law, our firm and about yourself.

Working with one of the world's leading practices also means more opportunities: the chance to try the things you want to try, work on secondments abroad or with clients, and get involved with headline making matters.

Enjoy every last bit of your training contract and develop the all round skills that all top lawyers need.

Visit our website for more details: www.dlapipergraduates.co.uk or follow us on Facebook.

www.dlapiper.com | DLA Piper UK LLP

EVERYTHING MATTERS

DLA Piper is a global law firm operating through various separate and distinct legal entities. Further details of these entities can be found at www.dlapiper.com

JULI2 | 2351974

Photocopying?
Tea run?
Data entry?
The usual humdrum?

Forget it.....

GRADUATE VACANCIES IN 2013

ENGINEERING

FINANCE

GENERAL MANAGEMENT

HUMAN RESOURCES

IT

MARKETING

SALES

NUMBER OF VACANCIES
Around 40 graduate jobs

LOCATIONS OF VACANCIES

STARTING SALARY FOR 2013
£27,000+
£35,000+ for Exploration and Production.

UNIVERSITY VISITS IN 2012-13
BIRMINGHAM, IMPERIAL COLLEGE
LONDON, LEEDS, LEICESTER,
LOUGHBOROUGH, MANCHESTER,
NOTTINGHAM, SHEFFIELD, WARWICK
Please check with your university careers service for full details of local events.

MINIMUM ENTRY REQUIREMENTS
2.1 Degree
Relevant degree required for some roles.

APPLICATION DEADLINE
Please see website for full details.

FURTHER INFORMATION
www.Top100GraduateEmployers.com
Register now for the latest news, events information and graduate recruitment details for Britain's leading employers.

Tens of millions of people across the world depend on E.ON for a safe, affordable and reliable energy supply. That's a big responsibility – and no mean feat. They rely on E.ON's 80,000 people to ensure the lights stay on, and that they're doing their bit for the environment.

At E.ON, graduates can change the future of energy. It's as simple as that. The world is transforming the way it produces and consumes energy in an unprecedented energy revolution – and successful applicants to E.ON will be part of it.

So where do graduates fit in? They can forget about photocopying and admin. Instead, they should expect high profile projects that will stretch them, challenge them and give them responsibility from day one. Along the way, they'll be given the chance to pick up professional qualifications and broad experience, as graduates rotate around the business, in the UK and internationally.

The learning comes thick and fast at E.ON – but then again, so does the support. Senior mentors are always on hand to help when things don't go quite right. There's training available on lots of different subjects too – everything from the latest developments in the energy markets to presentation skills, assertiveness and project management.

Graduates will be able to choose from a range of commercial and technical schemes covering different areas of the business. But all of them offer the chance to make a lasting impact on people's lives and the environment – and to play a part in the biggest energy revolution for a generation.

One of the best opportunities to change the world and make a real difference? Definitely.

...Don't just power up your laptop.

Power up your city.

We're right in the middle of an energy revolution.
It's smarter. It's extraordinary. It's global.
We need graduates that are too.

eon-uk.com/graduates

GRADUATE VACANCIES IN 2013
ENGINEERING
FINANCE
GENERAL MANAGEMENT
HUMAN RESOURCES

NUMBER OF VACANCIES
80 graduate jobs

LOCATIONS OF VACANCIES

STARTING SALARY FOR 2013
£25,500+
2013 pay review pending.

UNIVERSITY VISITS IN 2012-13
BATH, BIRMINGHAM, BRISTOL, CARDIFF,
IMPERIAL COLLEGE LONDON, LONDON
SCHOOL OF ECONOMICS, MANCHESTER,
OXFORD, SHEFFIELD, SOUTHAMPTON,
STRATHCLYDE, UNIVERSITY COLLEGE
LONDON, WARWICK
*Please check with your university careers
service for full details of local events.*

MINIMUM ENTRY REQUIREMENTS
2.1 Degree
Relevant degree required for some roles.

APPLICATION DEADLINE
January 2013

FURTHER INFORMATION
www.Top100GraduateEmployers.com
*Register now for the latest news, events
information and graduate recruitment
details for Britain's leading employers.*

In the years to come, the energy industry will face some of its greatest challenges. Climate change, security of supply, the need for new infrastructure – all of these will affect the way things are done. But as the largest generator of low carbon electricity in the UK, EDF Energy is perfectly placed to tackle such issues.

The graduates taken on now will help them to do just that; harnessing the potential of nuclear power to make a sustainable energy future a reality. It's a challenge. But more than that, it's a unique opportunity for graduates to gain the skills, experience and confidence they need to build a great career and to play a part in defining the UK energy industry for generations to come.

From civil, electrical, mechanical and chemical engineering; physics, chemistry and mathematics; finance, HR, supply chain and energy analysis; every one of their graduate schemes offers a structured programme with a variety of placements.

They're schemes designed to support, test and develop people who have the potential to be future industry leaders and to offer some of the most technically challenging, professionally inspiring, personally rewarding opportunities imaginable. All programmes feature a benefits package that is designed to match individual talents and reward contribution to the business.

With expertise in a wide range of energy sources and across many stages of the energy process, theirs is a unique proposition. One that will set the path to a bright and rewarding future and redefine the UK Energy Industry, shaping it for generations to come. Together with their commitment to reduce the intensity of CO_2 emissions from electricity production to 60% by 2020 and helping the UK meet its target of 80% reductions in CO_2 by 2050, it is a challenge like no other.

Because real heroes don't settle for second best.

The time has come to start pushing yourself further, to start applying the fresh creative thinking that will define the UK energy industry for generations to come. Perhaps you're up for the engineering challenge of building our nuclear future. Or maybe the commercial, logistical and human aspects of managing a fast-growing, fast-changing business are more your thing. It's all waiting at EDF Energy.

Find out more at
www.edfenergy.com/graduates

Ernst & Young is one of the world's leading professional services organisations, with a turnover of US $22.9billion. It currently has over 152,000 people in 140 countries and ambitious global growth plans. This continued growth depends on the talented, engaged and diverse people who drive its success.

Ernst & Young's clients include some of the world's most successful, innovative and respected organisations, spanning all industry sectors. Their people understand how businesses work. Their ingenuity and creativity help anticipate and meet their clients' needs; improving how they work, making vital business decisions and exploring opportunities. They work globally in four service lines: Advisory, Assurance, Corporate Finance and Tax.

Ernst & Young seeks out driven, ambitious graduates who want a stimulating and challenging start to their careers. Graduates can go further, faster, learning from the experts while working with diverse clients across industry sectors or specialising in financial services. All this experience is grounded in world-class training, mentoring and professional qualifications – the first step on a successful and varied career path.

Ernst & Young has graduate opportunities across the UK, and for first and second year degree students there are programmes and activities to improve their employability. Insight Days let them explore what it's really like to work for one of the world's leading professional services firms. Industrial Placements and Summer Internships also offer the chance to secure a graduate job before their final year. The Leadership Academy helps exceptional undergraduates recognise and use their strengths in a career that takes them to the top.

Ernst & Young provides an exceptional foundation in business and is one of the very best places to start a career.

GRADUATE VACANCIES IN 2013

ACCOUNTANCY
CONSULTING
FINANCE
IT

NUMBER OF VACANCIES
900 graduate jobs

LOCATIONS OF VACANCIES

STARTING SALARY FOR 2013
£Competitive

UNIVERSITY VISITS IN 2012-13
ABERDEEN, ASTON, BATH, BIRMINGHAM, BRISTOL, CAMBRIDGE, CARDIFF, CITY, DURHAM, EDINBURGH, EXETER, GLASGOW, IMPERIAL COLLEGE LONDON, KING'S COLLEGE LONDON, LANCASTER, LEEDS, LONDON SCHOOL OF ECONOMICS, LOUGHBOROUGH, MANCHESTER, NEWCASTLE, NOTTINGHAM, OXFORD, READING, SHEFFIELD, SOUTHAMPTON, ST ANDREWS, STRATHCLYDE, SURREY, UNIVERSITY COLLEGE LONDON, WARWICK, YORK
Please check with your university careers service for full details of local events.

MINIMUM ENTRY REQUIREMENTS
2.1 Degree
300 UCAS points

APPLICATION DEADLINE
Year-round recruitment
Early application advised.

FURTHER INFORMATION
www.Top100GraduateEmployers.com
Register now for the latest news, events information and graduate recruitment details for Britain's leading employers.

How can I go further, faster?

If you've got the drive and ambition to ask, then come and talk to us. Our clients across the world demand people with exceptional skills and knowledge to help them make vital business decisions every day. That's why we provide world-class mentoring, training and professional qualifications to take you from strength to strength.

Start a career that goes further, faster:
ey.com/uk/careers

ERNST & YOUNG
Quality In Everything We Do

GRADUATE VACANCIES IN 2013

ACCOUNTANCY

CONSULTING

FINANCE

LAW

MARKETING

RESEARCH & DEVELOPMENT

NUMBER OF VACANCIES
No fixed quota

LOCATIONS OF VACANCIES

Vacancies available in Europe.

STARTING SALARY FOR 2013
£41,500+

UNIVERSITY VISITS IN 2012-13
CAMBRIDGE, DURHAM, EDINBURGH, KING'S COLLEGE LONDON, KENT, LONDON SCHOOL OF ECONOMICS, MANCHESTER, NEWCASTLE, OXFORD, SHEFFIELD, ST ANDREWS, TRINITY COLLEGE DUBLIN, UNIVERSITY COLLEGE DUBLIN, WARWICK, YORK
Please check with your university careers service for full details of local events.

MINIMUM ENTRY REQUIREMENTS
Relevant degree required for some roles.

APPLICATION DEADLINE
Varies by function

FURTHER INFORMATION
www.Top100GraduateEmployers.com
Register now for the latest news, events information and graduate recruitment details for Britain's leading employers.

The European Commission plays a key role in shaping the lives and futures of 500 million people across the EU. Its staff form the largest contingent of the EU Civil Service, which is made up of around 50,000 people. As an international public sector organisation it offers a range of different career options, as well as the opportunity to travel and live abroad.

There are a wide variety of roles available as an EU civil servant, from specialist Lawyers and Economists, to generalist Policy Officers and Project Managers. The areas of policy and legislation that the EU deals with are also diverse – from Climate Change to Trade and from Financial Regulation to International Development. Specific examples of work range from negotiating trade agreements with countries such as China and the US to managing the delivery of projects that help the poorest regions across Europe.

Rather than being offered a set Graduate Programme, EU staff instead have the opportunity to drive the direction of their career allowing them to experience different policy areas. The EU Civil Service also offers numerous development opportunities including some of the best language training in the world.

Applications are made to a centralised recruitment process which leads to opportunities across the EU civil service, including within the Commission, as well as other EU Institutions and Agencies that combine to offer 'EU Careers'.

As well as permanent graduate positions, the European Commission (and other EU institutions) also offer twice-yearly paid traineeships which last five months and attract thousands of graduate applications from across Europe. These are a great way to experience life abroad – and to prepare for an application for a permanent EU Career.

Staff are located in Brussels, Luxembourg and offices around the world.

BE HONEST:
Some study
European history.
Can you make it?

The choice is yours.
Get just any job – or one where you can make a difference.
Make a real difference to the European Union. That's the challenge before us: ensuring that everything that happens across our 27 member states enhances the lives of 500 million citizens.
It's an enormous undertaking. One that requires only the best graduates. Graduates with real drive, commitment and passion to succeed. Graduates like you.
An EU citizen, you'll relish this opportunity to play a key role in policy formulation, operational delivery and resource management. Indeed, your contribution will have a direct impact on the European Union's success.

With a good knowledge of English, German and/or French, you'll have strong problem-solving abilities, good communication skills and know how to consistently deliver high quality results.

For more information, please visit
www.eu-careers.eu

As an international law firm, Freshfields Bruckhaus Deringer advises some of the world's most well known businesses. For graduates keen to pursue a career in commercial law, the firm offers challenging work that demands a strong intellect and a desire to help ambitious businesses achieve long-term success.

The firm provides clients with a global service from its network of offices across Europe, the Americas and Asia. It is essential that this service is consistent and of the highest quality.

Graduates who accept a training contract with the firm have the opportunity to experience up to eight areas of law – twice the number offered by most law firms. The training is largely provided from the firm's London office but many trainees will also spend time on secondment to a client or to one of the firm's US, European or Asian offices.

The lawyers work in teams, often of no more than three: a partner, an associate and a trainee. Whatever clients want to achieve, the team's job is to work out how. Is it possible? What will be the most effective way of structuring the deal or tackling the problem? What are the risks? How should it be documented? The team has to provide real commercial solutions, not just what is right or wrong in law.

Background, university, and the degree studied are immaterial. But every successful candidate has three qualities that are non-negotiable: intellectual talent, excellent English (written and verbal), and a generous spirit.

The firm pursues premium, cross-border work that is nearly always complicated. This means that the learning curve is steep, so the graduates who do best are those who like to be challenged.

GRADUATE VACANCIES IN 2013

LAW

NUMBER OF VACANCIES
100 graduate jobs
For training contracts starting in 2015.

LOCATIONS OF VACANCIES

STARTING SALARY FOR 2013
£39,000

UNIVERSITY VISITS IN 2012-13
ABERDEEN, BELFAST, BIRMINGHAM, BRISTOL, CAMBRIDGE, CARDIFF, CITY, DURHAM, EAST ANGLIA, EDINBURGH, ESSEX, EXETER, GLASGOW, KING'S COLLEGE LONDON, KENT, LANCASTER, LEEDS, LEICESTER, LIVERPOOL, LONDON SCHOOL OF ECONOMICS, MANCHESTER, NEWCASTLE, NORTHUMBRIA, NOTTINGHAM, OXFORD, QUEEN MARY LONDON, READING, SCHOOL OF AFRICAN STUDIES, SHEFFIELD, SOUTHAMPTON, ST ANDREWS, TRINITY COLLEGE DUBLIN, UNIVERSITY COLLEGE DUBLIN, UNIVERSITY COLLEGE LONDON, WARWICK, YORK
Please check with your university careers service for full details of local events.

APPLICATION DEADLINE
Law: 31st July 2013
Non-law: 1st May 2013

FURTHER INFORMATION
www.Top100GraduateEmployers.com
Register now for the latest news, events information and graduate recruitment details for Britain's leading employers.

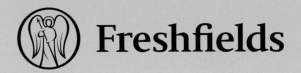 **Freshfields**

Where does
law
end AND
business
begin?

Many firms talk about 'commercial awareness' as if it's a nice-to-have. For us, it's much more than that. As a Freshfields lawyer, you will be advising your clients on the intricacies of their business. And that means you have to be genuinely interested in the commercial world: the complexities, the challenges, the people. Everything. That's what it means to be a commercial lawyer; and if you're interested, we can help you become one of the best.

Find out more and apply at
www.freshfields.com/uktrainees

www.ge.com/uk/careers

facebook.com/gecareers **f**   uk.careers@ge.com ✉

youtube.com/GEintheUK ▶   twitter.com/GECareers 🐦

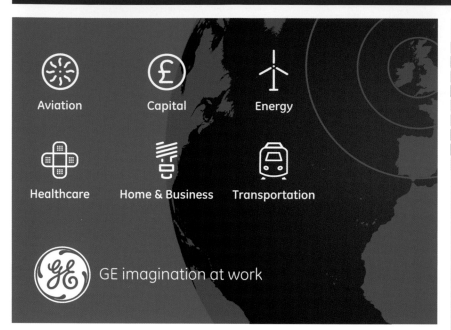

Aviation   Capital   Energy

Healthcare   Home & Business   Transportation

GE imagination at work

**Founded by Thomas Edison in 1878, GE is one of the world's
biggest and most valuable brands, operating in over 100
countries and employing 300,000 people worldwide.
In the UK alone, GE employs over 18,000 people across
60 major locations.**

GE has a long history of invention and innovation with a diverse portfolio –
from financial services and power generation, to aircraft engines and healthcare.
Its employees work on things that matter by building, powering, moving
and curing the world. Today, GE Technology will help doctors save 3,000
lives; a GE powered aircraft will take off every two seconds; GE Capital will
provide $1.5 billion in credit for businesses and GE Energy will create 25%
of the world's electricity.

Those who are successful in joining GE would become part of a dynamic
and talented global workforce, consistently rated No 1 for leadership. It is a
company where graduates have unique opportunities to learn, to develop and
to establish fantastic careers.

GE offers a variety of internships and graduate programmes covering
engineering, operations, research and development, IT, finance, HR and
marketing. The company seeks to attract those who are passionate, clear
thinkers and who work collaboratively to solve some of the world's most
challenging problems.

Graduates will gain exposure to some of the world's best business leaders,
expand their global mind-set and develop a diverse network of colleagues.
Development is through job assignments, classroom, e-learning and mentoring.
It can also include opportunities to travel abroad to work in one of GE's 100
locations around the world.

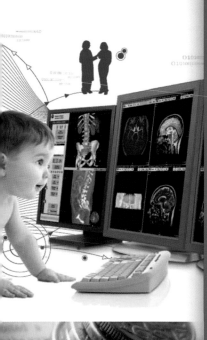

AT GE

we believe in the
POWER OF IDEAS
In taking them from bursts of
brilliance in the mind to

REVOLUTIONARY
TECHNOLOGIES
in the world.
WE'RE A TEAM
of engineers, scientists,
teachers, leaders and
doers united by a
COMMON GOAL:
Making things work better
for all. It's why we come to
work every day–to make
good on our mission to
POWER, MOVE,
BUILD AND CURE
THE WORLD.

Your Future Works
ge.co.uk/careers

GE imagination at work

GlaxoSmithKline

GRADUATE VACANCIES IN 2013

ENGINEERING

FINANCE

HUMAN RESOURCES

IT

MARKETING

PURCHASING

RESEARCH & DEVELOPMENT

SALES

NUMBER OF VACANCIES
50+ graduate jobs

LOCATIONS OF VACANCIES

STARTING SALARY FOR 2013
£Competitive

UNIVERSITY VISITS IN 2012-13
Please check with your university careers service for full details of local events.

MINIMUM ENTRY REQUIREMENTS
2.1 Degree
Relevant degree required for some roles.

APPLICATION DEADLINE
Year-round recruitment
Early application advised.

FURTHER INFORMATION
www.Top100GraduateEmployers.com
Register now for the latest news, events information and graduate recruitment details for Britain's leading employers.

One of the world's leading healthcare companies, GSK gives its people the chance to answer some of the planet's biggest questions. Questions about future healthcare needs and about building an innovative, global business to meet them, as well as questions about their personal and professional growth.

Dedicated to helping millions of people around the world to do more, feel better and live longer, GSK is revolutionising its business to meet changing healthcare needs from London to Lima, Lusaka, Luzhou and Lahore. GSK invested £3.96 billion in R&D in 2010 and topped the Access to Medicine Index, underlining its commitment to tackle some of the world's deadliest diseases by embracing new, open and innovative ways of working.

GSK discover, develop, manufacture and distribute vaccines, prescription medicines and consumer health products. Based in the UK, with operations in over 100 countries, GSK produce a huge range of healthcare products from lifesaving prescription medicines and vaccines to popular consumer products like Lucozade, Ribena, Sensodyne, Aquafresh and Panadol. In fact, every year GSK screen about 65 million compounds, make over four billion packs of medicines and healthcare products, and supply one quarter of the world's vaccines.

GSK is deeply committed to developing people through a range of ongoing development opportunities that includes tailored, 2-3 year rotational graduate programmes and industrial or summer placements. So it offers graduates the trust and respect to be themselves, and develop their careers across an incredibly diverse collection of businesses and geographies, in an environment where personal growth can play a vital part in the changing face of the business.

Most of all, GSK graduates enjoy the sense of purpose that comes from leading change in an industry that touches millions every day.

What are you looking for in your new career? The chance to make a name for yourself? Training? Development? Rewards? The chance to make a difference? All of the above?

Wouldn't it be great if a company could answer all those questions for you? And ask you to answer some of the biggest questions around? Like, what's the future of healthcare? What does a truly global business look like? And, how do you help millions of people worldwide to do more, feel better and live longer?

Are you a graduate with ambitions in Sales, Marketing, Communications, Finance, Science, IT, IT SAP, HR, Purchasing, Engineering or Health Outcomes? Or are you looking for a truly rewarding industrial placement? Have you visited www.gskbigquestions.com yet?

ANSWER THE BIG QUESTIONS

It takes different academic backgrounds to make an impact.

Learn more at goldmansachs.com/careers in

The Goldman Sachs Group, Inc. is a leading global investment banking, securities and investment management firm that provides a wide range of financial services to a substantial and diversified client base that includes corporations, financial institutions, governments and high-net-worth individuals.

The people of Goldman Sachs share a passion for achieving results and recognise that success comes with integrity. Their unique backgrounds, individual perspectives and diverse skills are put to the test as they help the firm's clients achieve their business goals.

Goldman Sachs is structured in a series of specialised divisions: Finance, Global Compliance, Global Investment Research, Human Capital Management, Internal Audit, Investment Banking, Investment Management, Legal, Merchant Banking, Operations, Securities, Services and Technology.

Nearly everyone – from the most senior leaders to junior analysts – is actively involved in recruiting as the goal is to recruit people who share the firm's core values. Academic achievement is important, but is only one indication of a person's potential.

Goldman Sachs recognises a diverse workforce encourages increased creativity and innovation. Diversity is crucial to improved performance and continued business success. To that end, the firm is committed to an environment that values diversity and promotes inclusion.

Academic discipline is less important to Goldman Sachs than the personal qualities an individual brings with them, however a strong interest in and appreciation of finance is important. Whatever the background may be, it is intellect, personality and zest for life that the company values the most.

GRADUATE VACANCIES IN 2013
ACCOUNTANCY
FINANCE
HUMAN RESOURCES
INVESTMENT BANKING
IT

NUMBER OF VACANCIES
300 graduate jobs

LOCATIONS OF VACANCIES

Vacancies also available in Europe, the USA, Asia and elsewhere in the world.

STARTING SALARY FOR 2013
£Competitive

UNIVERSITY VISITS IN 2012-13
BATH, BIRMINGHAM, BRISTOL, BRUNEL, CAMBRIDGE, CITY, DURHAM, EDINBURGH, GLASGOW, IMPERIAL COLLEGE LONDON, KING'S COLLEGE LONDON, LONDON SCHOOL OF ECONOMICS, LOUGHBOROUGH, MANCHESTER, NOTTINGHAM, OXFORD, SOUTHAMPTON, UNIVERSITY COLLEGE LONDON, WARWICK, YORK
Please check with your university careers service for full details of local events.

APPLICATION DEADLINE
28th October 2012

FURTHER INFORMATION
www.Top100GraduateEmployers.com
Register now for the latest news, events information and graduate recruitment details for Britain's leading employers.

Goldman Sachs

How will you make an impact?

Contribute, collaborate and succeed with a career at Goldman Sachs.

If you're the kind of person who can't wait to make a difference, consider a career at Goldman Sachs. We believe that good ideas and innovations can come from anyone, at any level. We offer meaningful opportunities, best-in-class training and a wide variety of career paths for talented people from all academic backgrounds. Plus, with access to important clients and projects, you'll have the chance to make an impact with global significance.

Application Deadlines
Full-Time: 28 October 2012
Summer Programme: 2 December 2012
Work Placement: 6 January 2013
Spring Programme: 6 January 2013

goldmansachs.com/careers

in

How to sum up an exciting business like Grant Thornton? Simply put, it is part of a global organisation delivering audit, tax and advisory services to dynamic organisations in over 100 countries. In the UK alone, it delivers solutions to 40,000 clients, across a broad range of sectors.

Getting right to the core of client needs and meeting them with clarity and insight is at the heart of Grant Thornton's business. In today's market, this combination of expertise, critical thinking and personal attention sets it apart.

Over 300 ambitious graduates, interns and placement students join Grant Thornton in over 20 of its 27 UK offices each year. They enjoy variety and responsibility from the start, working on client assignments from multinationals to fast-growth companies such as start ups. The learning curve is steep. Trainees can be leading their own team or portfolio by their second year. And with Grant Thornton's global reach there are plenty of opportunities for international exposure to clients and secondments.

Grant Thornton's structured training, varied on-the-ground client experience and supportive working environment gives trainees the chance to develop and grow as trusted advisers. Trainees will develop an understanding of business, as well as achieving a respected professional qualification and a competitive salary.

So what is Grant Thornton looking for? People with a passion for business, who combine reason and instinct to give the kind of advice that makes a real difference to the organisations it works with. Grant Thornton business advisers listen critically, dig deeper and have the confidence to challenge assumptions right from day one. They know it's about more than just the numbers, it's about enjoying tough challenges, seeking out opportunities and adding real value to clients by unlocking their potential for growth.

GRADUATE VACANCIES IN 2013
ACCOUNTANCY

NUMBER OF VACANCIES
300+ graduate jobs

LOCATIONS OF VACANCIES

STARTING SALARY FOR 2013
£Competitive

UNIVERSITY VISITS IN 2012-13
ASTON, BATH, BELFAST, BIRMINGHAM, BRISTOL, CAMBRIDGE, CARDIFF, DURHAM, EAST ANGLIA, EDINBURGH, EXETER, GLASGOW, IMPERIAL COLLEGE LONDON, KING'S COLLEGE LONDON, LANCASTER, LEEDS, LIVERPOOL, LONDON SCHOOL OF ECONOMICS, LOUGHBOROUGH, MANCHESTER, NEWCASTLE, NOTTINGHAM, OXFORD, READING, SHEFFIELD, SOUTHAMPTON, ST ANDREWS, STRATHCLYDE, UNIVERSITY COLLEGE LONDON, WARWICK, YORK
Please check with your university careers service for full details of local events.

MINIMUM ENTRY REQUIREMENTS
2.1 Degree
300 UCAS points

APPLICATION DEADLINE
31st January 2013
Early application advised.

FURTHER INFORMATION
www.Top100GraduateEmployers.com
Register now for the latest news, events information and graduate recruitment details for Britain's leading employers.

DON'T EAT YELLOW SNOW

What will your advice be?

Some advice just states the obvious. But the kind of insight that adds real value to dynamic organisations, such as our clients, takes reason, instinct and the confidence to challenge assumptions right from day one. You'll enjoy tough challenges, seek out opportunities and be ready to kick start a career as a trusted adviser right at the heart of business.

Sound like you? Here's our advice: visit
www.grant-thornton.co.uk/graduates

Grant Thornton

An instinct for growth™

Herbert Smith

Pre-eminent in dispute resolution and with an outstanding reputation for high value transactional advice, Herbert Smith LLP is a leading international law firm. Its main clients are prominent global and national businesses that it serves from offices in Asia, Europe and the Middle East.

In June 2012, Herbert Smith and Freehills' partnerships announced their decision to merge. At the time of going to print, they were targeting 1 October 2012 as the day on which they will combine to form a new firm, Herbert Smith Freehills. In addition to the Australia presence created by this merger, the firm is expanding its network in locations such as New York, South Korea and Germany, and is looking to establish a presence in Francophone Africa and Brazil.

Alongside Herbert Smith's outstanding reputation in dispute resolution and corporate work, the firm has leading practices in finance, real estate, competition and employment, pensions and incentives. It is also acknowledged as a leader in several industry sectors, including the energy and natural resources and financial institutions sectors.

The strength and breadth of the firm's practice areas guarantee excellent training and development opportunities for trainees. The training process balances contentious and non-contentious work; early responsibility and support. Trainees rotate around four six-month seats and are encouraged to go on secondment to a client or to one of the firm's international offices. Herbert Smith's global reach makes this a possibility for many.

Herbert Smith recruits from a variety of law and non-law degree backgrounds. As well as a strong academic record, applicants require a strong level of commercial awareness, the common sense to make their own way in a large firm and a creative and questioning mind.

GRADUATE VACANCIES IN 2013

LAW

NUMBER OF VACANCIES
85 graduate jobs
For training contracts starting in 2015.

LOCATIONS OF VACANCIES

Vacancies also available in Europe, Asia and elsewhere in the world.

STARTING SALARY FOR 2013
£38,000
Plus 25 days holiday.

UNIVERSITY VISITS IN 2012-13
BELFAST, BRISTOL, CAMBRIDGE, DURHAM, EDINBURGH, EXETER, IMPERIAL COLLEGE LONDON, KING'S COLLEGE LONDON, LONDON SCHOOL OF ECONOMICS, MANCHESTER, NOTTINGHAM, OXFORD, QUEEN MARY LONDON, SCHOOL OF AFRICAN STUDIES, SHEFFIELD, TRINITY COLLEGE DUBLIN, UNIVERSITY COLLEGE DUBLIN, UNIVERSITY COLLEGE LONDON, WARWICK
Please check with your university careers service for full details of local events.

MINIMUM ENTRY REQUIREMENTS
2.1 Degree

APPLICATION DEADLINE
Please see website for full details.

FURTHER INFORMATION
www.Top100GraduateEmployers.com
Register now for the latest news, events information and graduate recruitment details for Britain's leading employers.

Herbert Smith
Where do you see yourself in five years?
Train to be a lawyer at Herbert Smith and you'll work alongside some of the world's best legal minds and biggest companies. You'll also have the chance to expand your experience through international secondments to many exciting and vibrant emerging markets, which will provide you with endless opportunities to grow your career your way.
For more information on our training programme and vacation schemes, and for details on how to apply, visit:
www.herbertsmithgraduates.com

Hogan Lovells is a well-respected global top ten law firm, with over 40 offices worldwide. Its distinctive market position is founded on its exceptional breadth of practice, deep industry knowledge and a pragmatic commercial approach. It advises many of the world's largest corporations, financial institutions and government organisations.

Hogan Lovells' international strength across a wide range of practice areas gives them a strong reputation for corporate, finance, dispute resolution, government regulatory and intellectual property. The firm is known for encouraging supportive relationships among colleagues, particularly graduate trainees.

Trainees spend six months in four different areas of the practice to gain as much experience as possible. All trainees must spend six months in a corporate or finance group, and six months gaining contentious experience in the firm's litigation practice. There is also the opportunity to go on secondment to one of the firm's international offices or to one of its major clients in the second year of training. Trainees are offered as much responsibility as they can handle as well as a comprehensive skills training programme, regular reviews, appraisals and support. After qualification, continuous training and professional development remain a priority.

Hogan Lovells recruits up to 75 trainee solicitors per year and holds vacation schemes for first year law students, penultimate year law students and final year non-law students and graduates. Applications are welcome from both law and non-law students. The firm recruits candidates who can demonstrate strong academic and intellectual ability, ambition, drive, strong communication and interpersonal skills, a collaborative professional style and a sharp commercial attitude.

GRADUATE VACANCIES IN 2013

LAW

NUMBER OF VACANCIES
Up to 75 graduate jobs
For training contracts starting in 2015.

LOCATIONS OF VACANCIES

STARTING SALARY FOR 2013
£38,000

UNIVERSITY VISITS IN 2012-13
BELFAST, BIRMINGHAM, BRISTOL, CAMBRIDGE, CARDIFF, DURHAM, EDINBURGH, EXETER, KING'S COLLEGE LONDON, LEEDS, LONDON SCHOOL OF ECONOMICS, MANCHESTER, NEWCASTLE, NOTTINGHAM, OXFORD, SHEFFIELD, SOUTHAMPTON, ST ANDREWS, UNIVERSITY COLLEGE LONDON, WARWICK, YORK
Please check with your university careers service for full details of local events.

MINIMUM ENTRY REQUIREMENTS
2.1 Degree

APPLICATION DEADLINE
Law: 31st July 2013
Non-law: 30th April 2013

FURTHER INFORMATION
www.Top100GraduateEmployers.com
Register now for the latest news, events information and graduate recruitment details for Britain's leading employers.

GRADUATE VACANCIES IN 2013
FINANCE
GENERAL MANAGEMENT
INVESTMENT BANKING
IT
RETAILING

NUMBER OF VACANCIES
Around 450 graduate jobs

LOCATIONS OF VACANCIES

Vacancies also available in Europe, the USA and Asia.

STARTING SALARY FOR 2013
£Competitive
Plus a benefits package and discretionary bonus based on individual and business performance.

UNIVERSITY VISITS IN 2012-13
ASTON, BATH, BIRMINGHAM, BRISTOL, CAMBRIDGE, CITY, DURHAM, EDINBURGH, EXETER, GLASGOW, IMPERIAL COLLEGE LONDON, LEEDS, LEICESTER, LIVERPOOL, LONDON SCHOOL OF ECONOMICS, LOUGHBOROUGH, MANCHESTER, NOTTINGHAM, OXFORD, SHEFFIELD, SOUTHAMPTON, UNIVERSITY COLLEGE LONDON, WARWICK
Please check with your university careers service for full details of local events.

MINIMUM ENTRY REQUIREMENTS
2.1 Degree

APPLICATION DEADLINE
Varies by function
Please see website for full details.

FURTHER INFORMATION
www.Top100GraduateEmployers.com
Register now for the latest news, events information and graduate recruitment details for Britain's leading employers.

HSBC is one of the world's largest banking and financial services organisations. HSBC have 280,000 people that operate in 85 countries and territories, serving a customer base of around 89 million. They aim to be where the growth is, connect customers to opportunities and enable businesses to thrive and economies prosper.

Once, banks were built for North American and European finance. But traditional economies have started to shift while new markets emerge and old ones slow down. The world is changing the way it does business – and where it does business. HSBC has always looked in new directions to create teams, resources and relationships. With a strong global network that reaches into emerging economies and established markets, HSBC is shaped for the future.

At HSBC, there's always room for difference, but everyone shares a focus on teamwork, a feeling of community and mutual respect. It's a culture focused on doing the right thing where people take responsibility for their actions.

By focusing on the long term, HSBC can build on its achievements; look for new opportunities and never lose sight of its heritage. People are proud to be part of an organisation that's always moving forward – and doing so responsibly. Now, HSBC want people who share a focus on the bigger picture and are ready for the global challenges and opportunities that they offer.

For graduates, that means there's a platform for talent that offers global experience and exposure to new markets. The challenges are real and graduates become integral members of a network that stretches around the world. At HSBC, graduates can see past their short term goals to build long and rewarding careers.

Join the bank shaped for the future

The way the world does business is changing. At HSBC, we've invested in an economic future led by emerging markets and grounded in established economies. That's why we're looking for graduates with open minds, international perspectives and a focus on change. We can offer exposure to global markets and experience, training and experts that will prepare you for a long and successful career in banking.

Apply now to be part of the future of banking at
www.hsbcgraduatecareers.com

IBM

Been shopping today? IBM transformed retail with the Universal Product Code (UPC) – otherwise known as the bar code – over 40 years ago. The bar code now is a $17 billion dollar business, scanned billions of times each day.

DID YOU KNOW?

Malaria kills c800,000 people each year. In 2009 IBM launched 'SMS for Life' which enables health workers in hard-hit areas to order malaria medicine with a simple text message so they never run out of stock.

DID YOU KNOW?

IBM and innovation have always been great partners. Over the last 100 years, IBM has worked to make technology faster, more effective and more accessible. Today, they're focused on how they can make the planet a better place to work and live, by creating systems that improve people's lives.

Systems that can make energy grids more effective, improve water management, make healthcare more affordable and transform the global supply chain.

IBM employ talented, smart people in almost every area, in just about every country, so no matter where their talents and aspirations lie, it's not hard to find like-minded people who share their interests. At IBM graduates will gain knowledge and experience like nowhere else.

They'll also be challenged and supported to achieve everything they want in their career. And they'll find everything they need to build the kind of career they want. But it's up to them how it goes. They'll be the one in charge, putting forward their ideas, taking on responsibilities and making choices about how they get the job done.

To make sure graduates get exactly the help and skills they need, IBM provide targeted training that includes a range of opportunities – from a formal mentoring programme and tailored skills and career development to peer support and professional development through monthly forums and the IBM volunteering programme.

So it's no wonder that they've been voted 'Graduate Employer of Choice for IT' at The Times Graduate Recruitment Awards time and time again. Quite an achievement – but nothing compared to the great things their people go on to accomplish.

GRADUATE VACANCIES IN 2013

CONSULTING

FINANCE

IT

SALES

NUMBER OF VACANCIES
350 graduate jobs

LOCATIONS OF VACANCIES

STARTING SALARY FOR 2013
£29,000

UNIVERSITY VISITS IN 2012-13
ASTON, BATH, BELFAST, BIRMINGHAM, BRISTOL, CAMBRIDGE, CARDIFF, CITY, DURHAM, EDINBURGH, EXETER, GLASGOW, HULL, IMPERIAL COLLEGE LONDON, KING'S COLLEGE LONDON, KENT, LANCASTER, LEEDS, LIVERPOOL, LONDON SCHOOL OF ECONOMICS, LOUGHBOROUGH, MANCHESTER, NEWCASTLE, NOTTINGHAM, NOTTINGHAM TRENT, OXFORD, PLYMOUTH, QUEEN MARY LONDON, READING, ROYAL HOLLOWAY LONDON, SOUTHAMPTON, ST ANDREWS, STRATHCLYDE, SURREY, SUSSEX, UNIVERSITY COLLEGE LONDON, WARWICK, YORK
Please check with your university careers service for full details of local events.

MINIMUM ENTRY REQUIREMENTS
2.1 Degree

APPLICATION DEADLINE
Year-round recruitment
Early application advised.

FURTHER INFORMATION
www.Top100GraduateEmployers.com
Register now for the latest news, events information and graduate recruitment details for Britain's leading employers.

It's the survival of the smartest.

Join the best brains in business.

Right now, we are working to create a smarter planet. Integrating systems and technology to tackle the world's biggest challenges head on. From climate change to water conservation to the need for better, more innovative infrastructure. There's a lot to do, and we need people with ideas. People just like you.

Whether you join us in consulting, technology, business operations, sales, marketing or finance – on a gap year, summer internship, industrial placement or on our graduate programme – you'll gain the experience, skills and contacts you need to bring to life the smartest solutions to the toughest challenges.

Join us. Let's build a smarter planet. **ibm.com/jobs/uk**

Creating new products.
Exciting new careers.

From Shanghai to Sao Paolo, Jaguar Land Rover is a great British success story, designing, engineering, manufacturing and selling vehicles from two of the world's iconic premium brands. The UK's biggest exporter to China and Brazil, more than 80% of their products are exported abroad to global markets.

Jaguar Land Rover is making record profits, helping to fund significant investment in products and facilities. As the business grows, investing in people is key and the workforce has increased from 16,000 to more than 25,000 in the last two years. And their future has never been more exciting. At Jaguar Land Rover the graduate programme covers more than Product Development Engineering, with opportunities in everything from Manufacturing Engineering, Purchasing and Finance, to Human Resources, IT and Marketing, Sales & Service.

A dedication to excellence runs throughout the business. Wherever they're based, graduates have their innovation and creativity challenged, as they develop a rigorous and commercially-focused approach to their work. Training for professional qualifications as well as in-house training is provided to help them develop their business knowledge and personal skills. They will even spend time in the Lake District as part of their graduate induction programme, where they experience management development in awe-inspiring surroundings. And, at every stage of their careers, graduates are given the support and encouragement to reach their full potential.

For so many reasons, Jaguar Land Rover is the ultimate destination for graduates aspiring to build a world-class career. As would be expected from an internationally successful business, the rewards and benefits are outstanding and include a competitive salary and pension scheme, joining bonus and a discounted car purchase scheme.

ULTIMATEDESTINATION

Creating new products.
Exciting new careers.

GRADUATE OPPORTUNITIES

From Shanghai to Sao Paolo, Jaguar Land Rover is a great British success story. We design, engineer, manufacture and sell vehicles from two of the world's iconic premium brands. Although we are based in the UK, more than 80% of our products are exported abroad. We are the UK's biggest exporter to China and Brazil. Other successful markets include the USA, Middle East, South Africa, Russia, Australia as well as the UK and continental Europe. We are making record profits and this is helping to fund significant investment in our products and facilities for future growth. We believe that the future has never been more exciting.

At Jaguar Land Rover our graduate programme covers far more than just Product Development Engineering. There are opportunities in everything from Manufacturing Engineering, Purchasing and Finance, to Human Resources, IT and Marketing, Sales & Service.

Expectations and the demands will be high but you will be supported to realise your full potential. We will provide in-house training to help you develop your business knowledge and personal skills, as well as encouraging you to attain relevant professional qualifications. We will invest in you because we truly believe business is about people.

For full details, visit **www.jaguarlandrovercareers.com**

The John Lewis Partnership is one of the UK's largest retailers incorporating John Lewis Department Stores and Waitrose Supermarkets. Standing out in a competitive marketplace, they pride themselves on their unique approach – by combining integrity with the outstanding service that their customers trust.

The John Lewis Partnership has evolved a distinct brand of retailing that customers recognise and trust. Alongside this, they've grown to become experts in training, developing and nurturing graduates into some of the industry's most successful professionals and managers. Whilst John Lewis and Waitrose share principles of quality, service and value, they are distinct businesses working in different but equally challenging industry sectors.

The Partnership offers a range of exciting graduate schemes for ambitious individuals seeking early challenge and responsibility. The schemes include retail management for store-based managers of the future; head office roles, perfect for those who'd prefer to develop specialist expertise in key business support functions, and a challenging general management programme with insights into a range of business activities for those demonstrating exceptional leadership potential.

Because everyone who works for the John Lewis Partnership co-owns it as a Partner, graduates will find the opportunity to shape the way the business is run, share in its profits, and benefit from a host of exceptional benefits.

The John Lewis Partnership is looking for graduates who are ambitious, eager to learn, ready for a challenge, the kind of person who wants to get stuck in to the day to day running of a business as well as contribute to the long term strategic vision through real responsibility and challenges. Visit the website for more inspiration.

GRADUATE VACANCIES IN 2013
- FINANCE
- GENERAL MANAGEMENT
- PURCHASING
- RETAILING

NUMBER OF VACANCIES
40+ graduate jobs

LOCATIONS OF VACANCIES

STARTING SALARY FOR 2013
£25,000+

UNIVERSITY VISITS IN 2012-13
DURHAM, EDINBURGH, ESSEX, EXETER, HULL, LEEDS, LOUGHBOROUGH, MANCHESTER, NORTHUMBRIA, NOTTINGHAM, SWANSEA, WARWICK
Please check with your university careers service for full details of local events.

MINIMUM ENTRY REQUIREMENTS
Dependent on scheme
Please see website for full details.

APPLICATION DEADLINE
14th November 2012

FURTHER INFORMATION
www.Top100GraduateEmployers.com
Register now for the latest news, events information and graduate recruitment details for Britain's leading employers.

Graduate ambitions.
Great reputations.
The Partnership
starts here.

Graduate Schemes.

There's a good reason why Waitrose, John Lewis and our Head Office teams have gained such great reputations for quality and service. Everyone who works here co-owns our business as a Partner. It's why we're called the John Lewis Partnership – and if you join us on one of our graduate training schemes, you won't just find outstanding support and development. You'll get a say in the way we're run and a share in our profits too. Of course, this means more responsibility. We'll be expecting plenty of drive, initiative and fresh ideas from you. After all, that's what makes a great Partnership.

If you've got the potential to be a great Partner, and for more information about all our graduate schemes, visit **jlpjobs.com/graduates**

The John Lewis Partnership operates without discrimination and embraces diversity; this is reflected in all that we do.

cutting through complexity

www.kpmg.co.uk/times100

facebook.com/KPMGRecruitment uk-fmgraduates@kpmg.co.uk

linkedin.com/company/kpmg twitter.com/kpmgrecruitment

KPMG is a global network of professional firms providing Audit, Tax and Consultancy services to some of the world's biggest businesses. In the UK alone, KPMG has 22 offices and over 10,000 partners and staff. It has a diverse range of graduate programmes offering various professional qualifications.

KPMG believe in keeping their promises. It's what their business is built on. After all, when the world's biggest companies hand over their audit, tax or consulting challenges to KPMG, they need to know there's no margin for error.

Of course, the way to keep promises is to be clear about what will be delivered. So, for graduates, they offer exceptional training for professional qualifications (with an enviable pass rate few can match), tons of exposure and 'real world, real time' responsibility. But their graduates have to work for it – and certainly aren't running the show from day one. The fact is, they are grateful for that. It's a complex business, and it takes time – no matter how smart a graduate is – before they can really get their heads around it.

Of course, that's what also makes it such a stimulating place to be. For those who thrive on intellectual challenge, problem solving, working out the big picture through processing the details – and still having to think on their feet – it could be just the right place for them.

There's no one type of person that succeeds at KPMG though. It's a massively diverse business. There's room for all kinds of skills, qualities and experiences. Their clients operate in every business sector on the planet – and to give those clients the best service means providing them with experts who really understand them, whether that's an auditor, management consultant, tax specialist or technologist. As KPMG sees it, their people are absolutely at the heart of their continued success.

GRADUATE VACANCIES IN 2013
ACCOUNTANCY
CONSULTING
FINANCE
HUMAN RESOURCES
IT

NUMBER OF VACANCIES
800+ graduate jobs

LOCATIONS OF VACANCIES

STARTING SALARY FOR 2013
£Competitive

UNIVERSITY VISITS IN 2012-13
ABERDEEN, ASTON, BATH, BIRMINGHAM, CAMBRIDGE, CARDIFF, DURHAM, EDINBURGH, EXETER, GLASGOW, IMPERIAL COLLEGE LONDON, KING'S COLLEGE LONDON, LANCASTER, LEEDS, LEICESTER, LONDON SCHOOL OF ECONOMICS, LOUGHBOROUGH, MANCHESTER, NEWCASTLE, NOTTINGHAM, OXFORD, READING, SHEFFIELD, SOUTHAMPTON, ST ANDREWS, STRATHCLYDE, UNIVERSITY COLLEGE LONDON, WARWICK, YORK
Please check with your university careers service for full details of local events.

MINIMUM ENTRY REQUIREMENTS
2.1 Degree
320 UCAS points

APPLICATION DEADLINE
Year-round recruitment

FURTHER INFORMATION
www.Top100GraduateEmployers.com
Register now for the latest news, events information and graduate recruitment details for Britain's leading employers.

If you're not a little bit scared, you're not paying attention

You're about to enter the scary world of full time employment. And, chances are, you're not absolutely sure what to expect. Why would you be?

Unless you've grown up in a boardroom, things like dealing with corporate politics, working directly with big business clients, having to travel at short notice, having to report to someone, knowing when to express your opinion and when to keep schtum are unknown quantities to you right now. Rest assured though, at KPMG we get that, and will give you the training, development and support you need to deal with every aspect of your new working world.

We don't expect you to know it all from day one – just that you'll want to. And, actually, our graduates tell us working with us isn't all that different from being at university. We just wear nicer clothes.

To find out more go to kpmg.co.uk/times100

KPMG

cutting through complexity

KPMG
AWARDED No. 8 COMPANY
THE SUNDAY TIMES
25
BEST BIG
COMPANIES
TO WORK FOR
2012
KPMG

WE'VE GOT IT COVERED

GRADUATE VACANCIES IN 2013

ENGINEERING
FINANCE
LOGISTICS
MARKETING
RESEARCH & DEVELOPMENT
SALES

NUMBER OF VACANCIES
Around 20 graduate jobs

LOCATIONS OF VACANCIES

Vacancies also available in Europe.

STARTING SALARY FOR 2013
£27,000+
Joining bonus and annual performance bonus.

UNIVERSITY VISITS IN 2012-13
ASTON, BIRMINGHAM, DURHAM
Please check with your university careers service for full details of local events.

MINIMUM ENTRY REQUIREMENTS
2.1 Degree

APPLICATION DEADLINE
9th November 2012

FURTHER INFORMATION
www.Top100GraduateEmployers.com
Register now for the latest news, events information and graduate recruitment details for Britain's leading employers.

Kraft Foods has so many world-famous brands under wraps. For an ambitious graduate it's the chance to see behind the scenes of a global snacking powerhouse with an extraordinary presence in 70 countries – and explore the products that are adored by consumers and loved by colleagues everywhere.

This is more than just a graduate programme. It's a tailor-made experience for those with the passion to embrace the future, the commitment to drive for results and a head full of ideas ready to bring to life. No two days are ever the same in a series of exciting rotational placements across a variety of diverse brands, categories, and locations – from the UK & Ireland to the rest of Europe.

In whatever exhilarating part of the business, or the world, Kraft Foods graduates find themselves, the opportunities to learn, share ideas and champion change are limitless. Responsibility from day one, exceptional benefits and the chance to see hard work make an impact, it really is the perfect career package. What's more, they're continually pushed, pulled and ultimately rewarded as they progress.

When it comes to development it's all up for grabs. But it takes a challenging mix of hard work, focus and dedication to get there. It's a culture that's built on people so there's plenty of support too – with a buddy, mentor and many like-minded colleagues to join in the journey to success.

The desire to stand up and be counted, the motivation to keep improving, the commercial spirit that inspires great solutions – Kraft Foods graduates have it in bags. Together with the people skills that can make special things happen every day.

Kraft Foods has a proud tradition of developing outstanding future business leaders, who'll be uncovered as the next?

WHERE WILL YOU SEE THE BEST RESULTS?

WE'VE GOT IT COVERED

**Finance • Supply Chain • Engineering • Sales & Marketing
Industrial Placement Opportunities including RD&Q**

You know what you're capable of. You've studied hard, you know your own potential. You're ready to work your sweet wrappers off, stand up and be counted, drive results and bring those winning ideas to life. Welcome to Kraft Foods, a place where exciting changes are happening thanks to passionate people like you. We're not your average Times Top 100 company, this isn't your average graduate programme. Visit our website to find out more.

kraft foods

www.kraftfoodsgraduates.co.uk

Graduates joining the L'Oréal management training scheme will be given real responsibility, real challenges and real opportunities from day one. With 130 products sold per second worldwide, L'Oréal offers the most ambitious and entrepreneurial graduates the chance to work with, and become, the most inspirational minds in the business.

L'Oréal's stimulating, motivating and diverse culture is key in making it the No.1 FMCG employer of choice across Europe (Universum Student Survey, 2010). L'Oréal was awarded the 'Ethical Corporate Award 2011' for its innovative reporting in the area of responsible business and sustainable development.

With brands that reach over 1 billion people in more than 130 countries every year, L'Oréal's global scope is perfectly suited to interns, placement students and graduates pursuing exciting, international business careers. Over the course of a year, Management Trainees will work in three different areas of L'Oréal's business to help maximise their potential and prepare them for future leadership. In parallel to this, Management Trainees also benefit from a tailored development programme.

Across Marketing, Commercial, Supply Chain and Finance functions, Management Trainees could find themselves masterminding a launch strategy for one of its world renowned brands, such as Diesel or Armani, or negotiating with buyers at Britain's largest retailers. They could be tackling the logistical challenges presented by a company that produces over 4.5 billion products annually, or to managing part of L'Oréal's €20.3 billion revenue. Based in London, L'Oréal offers a host of excellent benefits, including healthcare, sports teams and fantastic social events. Completing an internship or placement year with L'Oréal is an excellent stepping stone onto the Management Trainee Scheme.

GRADUATE VACANCIES IN 2013
FINANCE
LOGISTICS
MARKETING
SALES

NUMBER OF VACANCIES
35 graduate jobs

LOCATIONS OF VACANCIES

STARTING SALARY FOR 2013
£28,000

UNIVERSITY VISITS IN 2012-13
BATH, CAMBRIDGE, CARDIFF, LANCASTER, LOUGHBOROUGH, MANCHESTER, NOTTINGHAM, OXFORD
Please check with your university careers service for full details of local events.

MINIMUM ENTRY REQUIREMENTS
2.1 Degree
320 UCAS points

APPLICATION DEADLINE
Year-round recruitment
Early application advised.

FURTHER INFORMATION
www.Top100GraduateEmployers.com
Register now for the latest news, events information and graduate recruitment details for Britain's leading employers.

As one of the UK's retail success stories, Lidl's simple retail philosophy and efficient working practices allow them to focus on what they do best – providing top quality products at the lowest possible prices. Their principles are clear structures, simple processes, flat hierarchies and short decision paths.

Lidl is an established international food retailer with more than 9,000 stores trading across Europe. With over 580 stores in the UK alone they have an impressive schedule of new store openings.

Uncompromising on quality, Lidl looks for the same in their graduates. Lidl is seeking talented, highly motivated and ambitious people who are excellent communicators and possess good commercial awareness. Lidl offer exciting opportunities for graduates to kick-start their career in a fast-paced environment, both within the UK and internationally.

The Graduate Area Management Programme is open to all degree disciplines and covers all aspects of retail management from store operations to logistics, supply chain, property and most importantly, people management. Additionally, the Buying and International Traineeship programmes are designed specifically for multilingual graduates and are tailored towards developing the personal, commercial and management skills needed to succeed. A structured and hands-on approach to training throughout all programmes, allows graduates to take on early responsibility with support being provided by experienced colleagues.

At Lidl, initiative is encouraged with achievements being recognised; this is supported by their promise that internal candidates come first for career opportunities. In fact, many of their senior professionals started their careers in store operations and have successfully progressed in career paths such as sales, property, construction, logistics and a wide range of head office positions.

GRADUATE VACANCIES IN 2013

GENERAL MANAGEMENT
PURCHASING
RETAILING
SALES

NUMBER OF VACANCIES
20 graduate jobs

LOCATIONS OF VACANCIES

STARTING SALARY FOR 2013
£33,000
With the potential to earn up to £53,000 per annum.

UNIVERSITY VISITS IN 2012-13
ASTON, BATH, BIRMINGHAM, DURHAM, EDINBURGH, EXETER, IMPERIAL COLLEGE LONDON, LANCASTER, LEEDS, MANCHESTER, NEWCASTLE, NORTHUMBRIA, NOTTINGHAM, NOTTINGHAM TRENT, OXFORD, READING, SOUTHAMPTON, ST ANDREWS, STRATHCLYDE, SURREY, SWANSEA, WARWICK
Please check with your university careers service for full details of local events.

MINIMUM ENTRY REQUIREMENTS
2.1 Degree

APPLICATION DEADLINE
Varies by function
Please see website for full details.

FURTHER INFORMATION
www.Top100GraduateEmployers.com
Register now for the latest news, events information and graduate recruitment details for Britain's leading employers.

Linklaters

Linklaters is one of the world's most prestigious law firms – a network of exceptionally talented, highly motivated lawyers, working as a team to become the leading global law firm. Linklaters pursues this ambition by building strong, long-term relationships with clients, colleagues and local communities.

While many law firms are strong in particular areas, Linklaters is the only firm to have market-leading global teams across the full range of corporate, finance and commercial practice areas. This, partnered with a culture of innovation, teamwork and entrepreneurship, means that Linklaters is asked to advise the world's leading companies, financial institutions and governments on their most important and challenging transactions and assignments.

With 19 practices across 27 cities, Linklaters gives graduates the opportunity to connect with a diverse range of international colleagues and clients on a daily basis. As part of the training contract, trainees have secondment opportunities to one of the firm's international offices or to a client's office.

Non-law graduates spend a conversion year at law school taking the Graduate Diploma in Law (GDL) and all graduates complete the Legal Practice Course (LPC) before starting their training contracts. The firm meets the cost and provides a maintenance grant for both. The training contract is structured around four six-month seats, designed to build knowledge, experience and contacts in a broad range of practice areas and to equip graduates for a long-term career.

Linklaters has high expectations of its trainees and recruits talented and motivated graduates. In return, they offer trainees global opportunities, world-class training and incredible rewards. Its commitment to training and development inspires its lawyers to become the best in the world.

GRADUATE VACANCIES IN 2013
LAW

NUMBER OF VACANCIES
110 graduate jobs
For training contracts starting in 2015.

LOCATIONS OF VACANCIES

Vacancies also available in Europe, the USA and Asia.

STARTING SALARY FOR 2013
£39,000

UNIVERSITY VISITS IN 2012-13
ABERDEEN, BIRMINGHAM, BRISTOL, CAMBRIDGE, CARDIFF, DURHAM, EDINBURGH, EXETER, GLASGOW, KING'S COLLEGE LONDON, LEEDS, LONDON SCHOOL OF ECONOMICS, MANCHESTER, NEWCASTLE, NOTTINGHAM, OXFORD, ST ANDREWS, UNIVERSITY COLLEGE LONDON, WARWICK, YORK
Please check with your university careers service for full details of local events.

MINIMUM ENTRY REQUIREMENTS
2.1 Degree

APPLICATION DEADLINE
Varies by function

FURTHER INFORMATION
www.Top100GraduateEmployers.com
Register now for the latest news, events information and graduate recruitment details for Britain's leading employers.

Linklaters
A career in law

Link up.

Looking for a career in law? At Linklaters, a law firm with 19 practice areas
in 27 cities across the globe, we look for talented and highly motivated
individuals to join our global network. So whether you are a law or non-law
student, link up with us for the opportunity to work in the most interesting
markets with the most prominent clients and on the most exciting deals.

To find out more about our training contracts and vacation schemes,
please visit

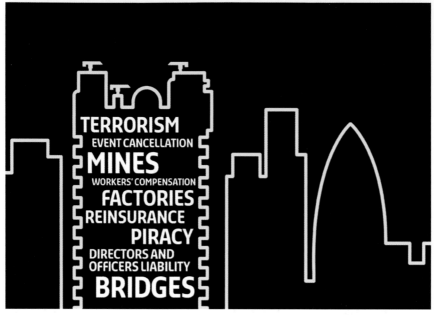

TERRORISM
EVENT CANCELLATION
MINES
WORKERS' COMPENSATION
FACTORIES
REINSURANCE
PIRACY
DIRECTORS AND
OFFICERS LIABILITY
BRIDGES

Lloyd's is the world's specialist insurance market. Lloyd's insure some of the world's most complex risks, from hurricanes to terrorism, sporting events to space travel, and celebrity body parts to Santa's beard. Based in London at One Lime Street, Lloyd's operates in more than 200 countries and territories around the world.

Lloyd's graduates can choose between the generalist programme and the claims programme. Or, for students who are in their penultimate year at university, they can join an eight-week summer internship programme.

Choosing their own placement areas, the generalist programme lets successful applicants explore the many roles Lloyd's has to offer. Graduates could be doing anything from managing relationships with international regulators, examining the potential impact of a catastrophe on Lloyd's, to helping corporate communications develop integrated marketing campaigns.

The claims graduate programme, meanwhile, offers sharp commercial thinkers the opportunity of fast-track development towards a career as a claims adjuster in the market. Ultimately the programme is designed to develop the future heads of claims.

Whichever graduate programme is chosen, they will work through a series of placements, working on live projects and taking on real responsibility. Of course, Lloyd's will make sure their graduates are up-to-speed on everything before they start, with a thorough induction, and continuous training and support throughout the programme.

Lloyd's are looking for graduates from any discipline, but they'll need good academics, plus they'll have razor-sharp analytical skills and the ability to think creatively.

LLOYDS BANKING GROUP

GRADUATE VACANCIES IN 2013

FINANCE
GENERAL MANAGEMENT
HUMAN RESOURCES
INVESTMENT BANKING
IT

NUMBER OF VACANCIES
220 graduate jobs

LOCATIONS OF VACANCIES

STARTING SALARY FOR 2013
£28,000-£38,000
£3,000 sign-on incentive.

UNIVERSITY VISITS IN 2012-13
ASTON, BATH, BIRMINGHAM, BRISTOL,
CAMBRIDGE, CARDIFF, CITY, DURHAM,
EDINBURGH, EXETER, IMPERIAL COLLEGE
LONDON, KING'S COLLEGE LONDON,
LANCASTER, LEEDS, LONDON SCHOOL
OF ECONOMICS, LOUGHBOROUGH,
MANCHESTER, NEWCASTLE, NOTTINGHAM,
OXFORD, QUEEN MARY LONDON,
SHEFFIELD, STRATHCLYDE, UNIVERSITY
COLLEGE LONDON, WARWICK, YORK
*Please check with your university careers
service for full details of local events.*

MINIMUM ENTRY REQUIREMENTS
2.1 Degree
260-320 UCAS points

APPLICATION DEADLINE
Varies by function

FURTHER INFORMATION
www.Top100GraduateEmployers.com
*Register now for the latest news, events
information and graduate recruitment
details for Britain's leading employers.*

Lloyds Banking Group is one of the UK's leading financial institutions. With multiple brands, including Lloyds TSB, Halifax and Bank of Scotland, one third of the population has a relationship with the Group. With such a diverse portfolio of brands, it has the range of career opportunities to match.

What underpins its entire business is a vision to become the UK's best bank for customers and shareholders. To do so, the Group is committed to creating better-value products and services, and strong, stable and sustainable returns.

The Group is also a place where talented individuals can fully explore their potential – and find a more rewarding career path. Because, as well as easy access to experienced senior professionals, graduates are given true autonomy to take their development to a new level. And with real responsibility from day one, there is plenty of opportunity to help shape one of the UK's largest financial organisations.

Here, graduates experience working in diverse business areas. At all times, the emphasis is on project ownership. Strong mentoring and support systems are in place, as well as formal training, and opportunities to study for internationally-renowned professional qualifications. Increasingly, the individuals who thrive in this environment are the ones who strive to create a positive impact through their own work, and that of others.

This year, the Lloyds Banking Group Graduate Leadership Programme includes roles in Finance, Human Resources, IT, General Management and Wholesale Banking & Markets. Each programme offers a unique experience – and every moment is an exciting opportunity – to make a difference and help Lloyds Banking Group become the UK's best bank for customers.

YOU'RE THE DIFFERENCE BETWEEN FOLLOW AND LEAD

I had to think on my feet to find the UK's next generation of leaders!

Graduate Opportunities

Raimee was surprised when we invited her to lead the launch of our Future Executives Programme for MBAs. Not just because she was fresh out of university, but because finding our future leaders meant working alongside some of our most senior leaders of today. In fact, moments like this are all part of the experience that awaits you on our Graduate Programme. Because, when it comes to making us the Best Bank for Customers – we know you can be the difference.

lloydsbankinggrouptalent.com

LLOYDS
BANKING
GROUP

 Lloyds TSB   HALIFAX   ✳ BANK OF SCOTLAND

Why start a career with M&S right now? Because right now is when it all begins, that's why. Smart technology, international growth, pioneering sustainability, fresh fashion, exclusive products – M&S is laying the foundations for an exciting future in every part of the business.

The M&S graduate programmes offer a range of prospects across different business areas. And the opportunities available, for those people who are willing to work hard to achieve the best for themselves and the business, are plentiful. For example, starting in retail management could lead to Commercial Manager level in 12 months, while the Head Office programme has roles in everything from IT and Food Technology to Merchandising and Logistics.

Wherever a graduate joins, the end of the programme will be the start of a career at M&S – one that will let them shape and grow the business. One that will allow them to see their achievements, and be proud of the work they accomplish.

Retail's moving faster than ever. What's cutting-edge right now will be old hat in five, three, even a year's time. And it's the graduates who arrive at M&S right now who'll be turning today's trends into tomorrow's reality. Whether that's in the way customers shop, the products and services on offer, or how M&S operates as an ethical brand in a changing world. That's the opportunity for those setting out on their career. It's exciting stuff.

Above all, graduates with high standards, a hard work ethic and commitment to doing the right thing for customers and colleagues won't have to wait to feel the benefit of working for a leading employer like M&S. Not just a competitive salary and the essential benefits expected from a global brand, but also a range of flexible rewards tailored to each individual's needs. There's no time like now.

GRADUATE VACANCIES IN 2013
GENERAL MANAGEMENT
HUMAN RESOURCES
IT
LOGISTICS
MARKETING
PURCHASING
RESEARCH & DEVELOPMENT
RETAILING

NUMBER OF VACANCIES
200 graduate jobs

LOCATIONS OF VACANCIES

STARTING SALARY FOR 2013
£23,500-£28,000
Plus benefits for the graduate scheme and £17,500 if graduates join on a placement.

UNIVERSITY VISITS IN 2012-13
ASTON, BATH, BIRMINGHAM, BRUNEL, CAMBRIDGE, CARDIFF, EAST ANGLIA, LANCASTER, LEEDS, LEICESTER, LOUGHBOROUGH, MANCHESTER, NEWCASTLE, NORTHUMBRIA, NOTTINGHAM TRENT, OXFORD, OXFORD BROOKES, READING, STRATHCLYDE, SURREY, SUSSEX
Please check with your university careers service for full details of local events.

MINIMUM ENTRY REQUIREMENTS
2.1 Degree

APPLICATION DEADLINE
December 2012

FURTHER INFORMATION
www.Top100GraduateEmployers.com
Register now for the latest news, events information and graduate recruitment details for Britain's leading employers.

MARS

www.mars.co.uk/graduates

twitter.com/marsgradsuk 🐦 facebook.com/marsgradsuk f

MAKE IT MEAN MORE

Think 'work, rest and play'. Think M&M's, Uncle Ben's, Pedigree, Whiskas and Wrigley, iconic billion-dollar brands. Think the world's third-largest food company with international operations in 370 locations. Know what makes Mars special? Think again.

Sure Mars is one of the world's leading confectionery companies and one of the world's leading petcare companies, but it's more like a community than a corporate. Because it's still privately owned. And that means it's a place without any of the trappings of typical big business. It has a sense of humanity and a lack of vanity around leadership. It's somewhere that encourages open communication and collaboration, where people can get to grips with challenging work and take on high levels of responsibility early on.

The flat, open structure is a big plus for graduates when it comes to grabbing the opportunity to shape Mars' business. It makes for a truly creative and dynamic environment. But it takes more than just freedom and responsibility to create Mars leaders. What you get is high levels of responsibility, a variety of possibilities and the opportunity to improve things for everyone else along the way.

Mars provides a fantastic support structure, financial sponsorship to pursue professional qualifications, extensive learning and development opportunities and personal mentoring from some of the brightest and best people in the industry. And the business expects its associates to use those things to achieve more. To make their performance mean more for themselves, improve the lives of others and benefit the planet.

Because, ultimately, what makes Mars special is the fact that it offers its associates the opportunity to grab life and make a lasting difference.

GRADUATE VACANCIES IN 2013
ENGINEERING
FINANCE
GENERAL MANAGEMENT
PURCHASING
RESEARCH & DEVELOPMENT

NUMBER OF VACANCIES
Around 25 graduate jobs

LOCATIONS OF VACANCIES

STARTING SALARY FOR 2013
£29,000-£31,000

UNIVERSITY VISITS IN 2012-13
Please check with your university careers service for full details of local events.

MINIMUM ENTRY REQUIREMENTS
2.1 Degree
300 UCAS points

APPLICATION DEADLINE
February 2013

FURTHER INFORMATION
www.Top100GraduateEmployers.com
Register now for the latest news, events information and graduate recruitment details for Britain's leading employers.

The M&S
of tomorrow.
Starting
today.

FLEXIBLE, PLANET-FRIENDLY
DIGITAL DISPLAYS WILL
REPLACE PRINTED SIGNAGE.

VIRTUAL REALITY WILL LET YOU
TRY CLOTHES ON WITHOUT
GETTING CHANGED.

GOODBYE CREDIT CARDS.
SMARTPHONES WILL BE
THE WAY TO PAY.

At M&S, we're laying the foundations
for an exciting future in every part
of our business. New technology,
international growth, industry-leading
sustainability plans and fresh fashion
are just some of the things you can
look forward to when you join us.
So, show us your ambition today
and tomorrow...well, tomorrow will
be whatever you make it. Let's go.

marksandspencer.com/gradcareers

THINK AHEAD WITH THE M&S GRADUATE PROGRAMMES

YOUR M&S

MARS

MAKE IT MEAN MORE

GRADUATE VACANCIES IN 2013
ENGINEERING
FINANCE
GENERAL MANAGEMENT
PURCHASING
RESEARCH & DEVELOPMENT

NUMBER OF VACANCIES
Around 25 graduate jobs

LOCATIONS OF VACANCIES

STARTING SALARY FOR 2013
£29,000-£31,000

UNIVERSITY VISITS IN 2012-13
Please check with your university careers service for full details of local events.

MINIMUM ENTRY REQUIREMENTS
2.1 Degree
300 UCAS points

APPLICATION DEADLINE
February 2013

FURTHER INFORMATION
www.Top100GraduateEmployers.com
Register now for the latest news, events information and graduate recruitment details for Britain's leading employers.

Think 'work, rest and play'. Think M&M's, Uncle Ben's, Pedigree, Whiskas and Wrigley, iconic billion-dollar brands. Think the world's third-largest food company with international operations in 370 locations. Know what makes Mars special? Think again.

Sure Mars is one of the world's leading confectionery companies and one of the world's leading petcare companies, but it's more like a community than a corporate. Because it's still privately owned. And that means it's a place without any of the trappings of typical big business. It has a sense of humanity and a lack of vanity around leadership. It's somewhere that encourages open communication and collaboration, where people can get to grips with challenging work and take on high levels of responsibility early on.

The flat, open structure is a big plus for graduates when it comes to grabbing the opportunity to shape Mars' business. It makes for a truly creative and dynamic environment. But it takes more than just freedom and responsibility to create Mars leaders. What you get is high levels of responsibility, a variety of possibilities and the opportunity to improve things for everyone else along the way.

Mars provides a fantastic support structure, financial sponsorship to pursue professional qualifications, extensive learning and development opportunities and personal mentoring from some of the brightest and best people in the industry. And the business expects its associates to use those things to achieve more. To make their performance mean more for themselves, improve the lives of others and benefit the planet.

Because, ultimately, what makes Mars special is the fact that it offers its associates the opportunity to grab life and make a lasting difference.

We found new ways to pounce on the mouse.

We'll go the extra mile to get results. Turns out that wasn't far enough for our graduate James. You see, when we planned to take Whiskas marketing into the digital space, we aimed to click in the UK. But as a graduate on our Mars Management Development Programme, James was bolder. He wanted global buzz. And to build a powerhouse brand online. Who were we to argue? Strategy, PR, media planning, developing creative assets. You name it, James got involved in it. Forget the fact that he'd barely been with us for a year. Because along the way his work amassed an army of online fans. From all around the world. And he turned a project valued at £200k into a £2m one. Just goes to show, give people freedom and responsibility and they'll go further than you ever imagined. **mars.co.uk/graduates**

MAKE IT MEAN MORE | **MARS**

McDonald's invests over £43 million in development programmes for its employees each year. The company has a proven track record of career progression, in fact the entire UK Operations executive team started off working in one of its restaurants. Prospective employees can be reassured that they can create a long-term career with one of the world's most recognised brands.

McDonald's has operated in the UK since 1974. The business is growing constantly and currently operates 1,200 restaurants, employing 87,500 employees.

The company's 20 week trainee management development programme gives participants a large amount of responsibility early on, exposing them to different organisational functions including management, operations, finance, human resources, marketing, and customer relations. Successful candidates work towards managing all aspects of a multimillion-pound business with an average of 80 employees.

The rewards are plentiful. The candidates will partake in a structured training and development programme which will help to fast-track their careers. They'll be eligible for a host of benefits including a quarterly bonus scheme (on completion of the programme), six weeks holiday, meal allowance, and private healthcare.

Working for a progressive company has its perks – there are opportunities to move to other UK locations in the future, or perhaps to do a secondment in McDonald's head office. For Trainee Business Managers who are logical thinkers, have a great attitude and are tenacious, energetic and hardworking, the opportunities are endless. With a range of benefits and future career prospects, graduates can find whatever they're looking for with a career at McDonald's.

GRADUATE VACANCIES IN 2013
GENERAL MANAGEMENT
RETAILING

NUMBER OF VACANCIES
100-150 graduate jobs

LOCATIONS OF VACANCIES

STARTING SALARY FOR 2013
£18,500-£21,500
Plus a quarterly bonus scheme and a meal allowance.

UNIVERSITY VISITS IN 2012-13
NOTTINGHAM TRENT
Please check with your university careers service for full details of local events.

MINIMUM ENTRY REQUIREMENTS
Relevant degree required for some roles.

APPLICATION DEADLINE
Year-round recruitment

FURTHER INFORMATION
www.Top100GraduateEmployers.com
Register now for the latest news, events information and graduate recruitment details for Britain's leading employers.

I CHOSE THE
CAREER THAT
OFFERED
THE BEST

OPPORTUNITY

TO PROGRESS
QUICKLY.

Janette
Business Manager

I worked at McDonald's part-time
whilst I was studying law. When
I graduated I chose to work here
full-time as a Trainee Business
Manager. They offer a great salary,
benefits package and a renowned
20-week Management Development
Program. They really helped me
to develop my skills and now
I'm a Business Manager. I love
working here and hope to progress
further and work in training or even
become a Franchisee.

To find out more about working
and learning with us visit
mcdonalds.co.uk/people

McKinsey&Company

McKinsey & Company helps world-leading clients in the public, private and third sectors to meet their biggest strategic, operational and organisational challenges. Their goal is to provide distinctive and long-lasting performance improvements – in short, it is about having an impact. Making a difference.

As a consultant in this truly global firm, graduates will have the opportunity to work with colleagues and clients from all around the world. They will come into contact with CEOs, government leaders and the foremost charitable organisations, and work together with them on their most exciting and challenging issues.

Working as part of a small team, and dedicated to one project at a time, graduates will be fully involved from the very start of their first project. No two weeks will be the same: from gathering and analysing data, to interviewing stakeholders or presenting findings to clients, the range of industries and business issues to which successful applicants have exposure will mean that they are constantly acquiring new skills and experience. Bright, motivated newcomers can expect their ideas and opinions to be encouraged and valued, right from day one.

Graduates will also enjoy world-class personal and professional development. Formal training programmes, coupled with a culture of mentoring and coaching, will provide the best possible support.

Working in consulting is challenging, but McKinsey encourages a healthy work-life balance. Successful applicants will find like-minded individuals, and a thriving range of groups, initiatives and events that bring people together.

McKinsey & Company is welcoming applications for both full time and summer internship applications. The deadline for both is October 31st 2012.

GRADUATE VACANCIES IN 2013

CONSULTING

NUMBER OF VACANCIES
No fixed quota

LOCATIONS OF VACANCIES

STARTING SALARY FOR 2013
£Competitive

UNIVERSITY VISITS IN 2012-13
BATH, BELFAST, BRISTOL, CAMBRIDGE, EDINBURGH, IMPERIAL COLLEGE LONDON, LONDON SCHOOL OF ECONOMICS, NOTTINGHAM, OXFORD, ST ANDREWS, TRINITY COLLEGE DUBLIN, UNIVERSITY COLLEGE DUBLIN, UNIVERSITY COLLEGE LONDON, WARWICK
Please check with your university careers service for full details of local events.

MINIMUM ENTRY REQUIREMENTS
2.1 Degree

APPLICATION DEADLINE
31st October 2012

FURTHER INFORMATION
www.Top100GraduateEmployers.com
Register now for the latest news, events information and graduate recruitment details for Britain's leading employers.

McKinsey&Company

Developing
global leaders

We welcome applications from all degree disciplines with
a minimum of 2.1 (expected or actual). To find out more
please visit www.mckinsey.com/careers

Home to around 7.5 million people and covering 620 square miles, London presents an ever-evolving challenge for the Metropolitan Police Service (MPS). In this most vibrant and complex of cities, the MPS fights to reduce crime – and the fear of crime – through world-class policing.

With over 30,000 officers and thousands more police staff and volunteers; the MPS is one of London's largest employers. Working on the frontline with the people of London is one of the most important, rewarding and absorbing roles around. But it's the host of people working behind the scenes who make it possible for officers to tackle the day-to-day challenges of policing one of the world's largest cities. It's a task that calls for the talents, passion, drive and commitment of all kinds of people, from all kinds of backgrounds.

Human Resources; IT & Technology; Marketing; Forensics: these are just a few of the departments that help the MPS to fight crime and police the capital. Many of these teams are to be found in any large company. But at the MPS, they are essential elements of the wider service, ensuring the organisation performs at its best. Thanks to the variety of areas, there's a wide range of roles on offer – all of which come with the in-depth training required to develop and progress.

The career of every officer and member of staff follows a different path. Working for the MPS can open doors to a multitude of areas such as police community support officers (PCSOs), special constables (volunteer police officers) and other volunteer roles offering yet more exciting opportunities.

An exceptionally rewarding career awaits every new recruit; one that will see them make a difference to the lives of millions of Londoners.

GRADUATE VACANCIES IN 2013
ACCOUNTANCY
FINANCE
GENERAL MANAGEMENT
HUMAN RESOURCES
IT
LAW
MARKETING
MEDIA
RESEARCH & DEVELOPMENT

NUMBER OF VACANCIES
To be confirmed

LOCATIONS OF VACANCIES

STARTING SALARY FOR 2013
£Competitive

UNIVERSITY VISITS IN 2012-13
LONDON
Please check with your university careers service for full details of local events.

APPLICATION DEADLINE
Year-round recruitment

FURTHER INFORMATION
www.Top100GraduateEmployers.com
Register now for the latest news, events information and graduate recruitment details for Britain's leading employers.

THE EVIDENCE
IS CLEAR.

There's no graduate programme like the Met graduate programme.

For the first time ever, we're launching a structured graduate programme for the next generation of Met police officers. Like London itself, it's demanding, world-class and brings out the best in ambitious people. It's also totally unique. But don't just take our word for it. Discover the evidence for yourself.

www.metpolicecareers.co.uk/graduates

NEW SCOTLAND YARD

METROPOLITAN POLICE **TOTAL POLICING**

SECURITYSERVICE
MI5

MI5 safeguards the UK against threats to national security including terrorism, espionage, cyber attack and the spread of weapons of mass destruction. It investigates suspect individuals and organisations to collate and analyse secret intelligence relating to these threats.

MI5's work requires highly capable, persuasive and analytical graduates from a range of backgrounds and degrees. Many join as Intelligence Officers, where postings may take graduates to legal, policy or resources departments. There are opportunities to work in the regional offices or Northern Ireland as well as on investigations. Exposure to a broad spectrum of MI5's work increases promotion prospects.

Others join as Intelligence Analysts, in IT Security or Network Forensics roles or in the Language Unit. Together they work on investigations assessing threats, analysing data, identifying patterns, making connections or solving complex digital intelligence problems.

The culture at MI5 is professional, friendly and informal. Honesty and integrity are expected from all members of staff. Teamworking, communication, problem solving, decision making and organisation skills are vital. Attention to detail, patience, sound judgement and commitment to self-development are also important.

Although MI5 does not offer a bespoke graduate programme, it provides extensive training and development opportunities. MI5 offers a generous holiday entitlement, pension and flexible working where operational commitments allow. Some sites have subsidised fitness facilities and staff restaurants. Applicants must be British citizens and limit those they tell about their application to immediate family and/or their partner.

GRADUATE VACANCIES IN 2013
FINANCE
GENERAL MANAGEMENT
HUMAN RESOURCES
IT
LAW

NUMBER OF VACANCIES
To be confirmed

LOCATIONS OF VACANCIES

STARTING SALARY FOR 2013
£24,750
£27,250 for IT roles.

UNIVERSITY VISITS IN 2012-13
Please check with your university careers service for full details of local events.

MINIMUM ENTRY REQUIREMENTS
2.1 Degree

APPLICATION DEADLINE
Year-round recruitment
Early application advised.

FURTHER INFORMATION
www.Top100GraduateEmployers.com
Register now for the latest news, events information and graduate recruitment details for Britain's leading employers.

Graduate opportunities
UK-based

Safeguarding the UK against threats to national security requires talented people. We recruit graduates with the potential to increase the skills within our organisation, to make it even more effective. Our staff comes from an increasingly diverse range of backgrounds and this in-depth understanding of different communities, cultures and languages is crucial for our work.
What unique talents could you bring to help protect the UK?

Find out more at **www.mi5.gov.uk/careers**

To apply you must be a British citizen. Discretion is vital. You should not discuss your application, other than with your partner or a close family member.

SECURITYSERVICE
MI5

Microsoft

Microsoft is the world leader in personal and business software, services and internet technologies. New perspectives, tastes and ambitions fuel the innovation that makes this happen – which makes graduates and interns vital to the future of the business.

Join Microsoft and work where the opportunity to stretch existing skills and build new ones is a given. Where new thoughts, ideas and experiences are welcomed, valued and rewarded. Where creating new technologies that will change the way the world works are the order of the day, every day.

Realising that developing the right people is the future of the business, Microsoft has created something special to give graduates from all degree disciplines a flying start to their career. It's called the Microsoft Academy for College Hires (MACH) scheme. It lasts for two years and aims to be the perfect bridge between academic and professional life, as well as the ideal preparation for future leaders of Microsoft.

As part of either the Sales or Technical scheme, MACH graduates will have the opportunity to shape their career. Working on major projects from day one, and with continuous mentor support and assessment to guide and encourage them, MACHs can tailor their development to match their aspirations. As well as learning from senior colleagues from across the business, they'll have the chance to meet other MACH graduates from around the world on a number of international networking events.

Microsoft also runs an award-winning Internship scheme for undergraduates. With a comprehensive induction followed by on-the-job learning, bespoke skills training and one-to-one performance reviews, it's an insightful introduction to the Microsoft business and paves the way to get ahead on the MACH scheme.

GRADUATE VACANCIES IN 2013
IT
SALES

NUMBER OF VACANCIES
45 graduate jobs

LOCATIONS OF VACANCIES

STARTING SALARY FOR 2013
£Competitive

UNIVERSITY VISITS IN 2012-13
ASTON, BATH, BIRMINGHAM, BRUNEL, CAMBRIDGE, CARDIFF, IMPERIAL COLLEGE LONDON, LOUGHBOROUGH, MANCHESTER, OXFORD, OXFORD BROOKES, READING, SURREY, UNIVERSITY COLLEGE LONDON, WARWICK
Please check with your university careers service for full details of local events.

MINIMUM ENTRY REQUIREMENTS
2.1 Degree
320 UCAS points

APPLICATION DEADLINE
30th November 2012

FURTHER INFORMATION
www.Top100GraduateEmployers.com
Register now for the latest news, events information and graduate recruitment details for Britain's leading employers.

What makes you will make Microsoft

Microsoft

UK Graduates

Andy loves technology, travel, Inter Milan and Kanye West. He's perfect for Microsoft because our success is built on the tastes, aspirations and ideas of individuals.

Whatever you're studying, bring your unique perspective to Microsoft and we'll give you the power to shape your own career. To find out more about our graduate and intern schemes, visit **www.microsoft.com/uk/graduates**

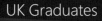

Get the free mobile app for your phone
http://gettag.mobi

Morgan Stanley

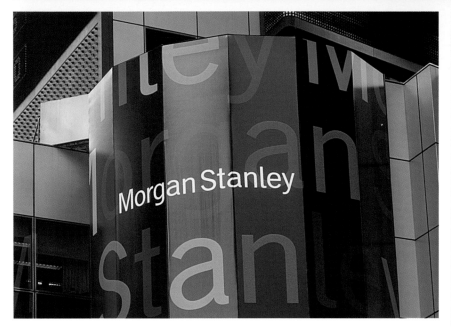

Morgan Stanley has a distinguished history of serving clients for over 75 years. Since its founding in 1935, the firm has been known for the important clients it serves, its innovative approach to solving complex problems, and its agility in embracing change.

Morgan Stanley is a firm that inspires people to be their best – and always finds new opportunities to offer them. Its mission is to build a community of talent that can deliver the finest financial thinking and products in the world.

There is no typical person at Morgan Stanley. People come from a wide variety of backgrounds and interests – all are high achievers who share integrity, intellectual curiosity and the desire to work in a collegial environment. Individuality is prized and people are encouraged to be themselves.

Morgan Stanley offers a variety of Graduate Programmes and internship opportunities for students who demonstrate the entrepreneurial drive, team working and communication skills to take the business forward. All Graduate Programmes are designed to provide graduates with the knowledge and toolkit they require to quickly become effective and successful professionals in their chosen area. Training is not limited to the first weeks or months on the job but continues throughout the graduate's career.

The summer and industrial placement programmes are considered first class and designed to attract, develop and continually assess those students who are most likely to succeed in the long-term. Through classroom-based and on-the-job training, seminars, regular mentoring, social events and the experience of working with top people in the industry throughout a period of either 10 or 48 weeks, students gain a unique insight into the industry and Morgan Stanley's culture – all necessary foundations for a truly exceptional and rewarding career.

GRADUATE VACANCIES IN 2013

FINANCE
HUMAN RESOURCES
INVESTMENT BANKING
IT

NUMBER OF VACANCIES
250-300 graduate jobs

LOCATIONS OF VACANCIES

Vacancies also available in Europe.

STARTING SALARY FOR 2013
£Competitive
Plus a discretionary bonus.

UNIVERSITY VISITS IN 2012-13
BATH, BELFAST, BRISTOL, CAMBRIDGE, CITY, DURHAM, EDINBURGH, GLASGOW, HERIOT-WATT, IMPERIAL COLLEGE LONDON, KING'S COLLEGE LONDON, LONDON SCHOOL OF ECONOMICS, LOUGHBOROUGH, NOTTINGHAM, OXFORD, ST ANDREWS, STIRLING, STRATHCLYDE, ULSTER, UNIVERSITY COLLEGE LONDON, WARWICK
Please check with your university careers service for full details of local events.

MINIMUM ENTRY REQUIREMENTS
2.1 Degree
320 UCAS points

APPLICATION DEADLINE
Varies by function
Please see website for full details.

FURTHER INFORMATION
www.Top100GraduateEmployers.com
Register now for the latest news, events information and graduate recruitment details for Britain's leading employers.

YOU HAVE TALENTS. WE HAVE OPTIONS.
NETWORKER
INFLUENCER
MENTOR
PIONEER
VISIONARY
Morgan Stanley
For more details visit our website
www.morganstanley.com/careers
Morgan Stanley is an equal opportunity employer committed to workforce diversity. (M/F/D/V) © 2012 Morgan Stanley

national**grid**

Help us keep everyone connected.

National Grid is one of the world's largest investor-owned energy companies and will be investing £16bn through to 2015 to secure the energy supply for future generations. They are looking for individuals who have great academic qualifications combined with strong personal/behavioural capabilities.

National Grid's role is to connect people to the energy they use. Society relies on having energy at its fingertips: it is built on it and National Grid owns and manages the systems to which many different energy sources are connected. In Britain they run systems that deliver gas and electricity across the entire country. In the North Eastern states of the US, they provide power directly to millions of customers. Holding a vital position at the centre of the energy system, National Grid join's everything up.

The energy market will dramatically change between now and 2015 and National Grid will play a vital role in connecting new sources of energy generation. The transition to a low carbon economy is set against a background of increasing population, changing economic times and ageing power plants will be unprecedented. This presents individuals with a tremendous opportunity to work with the latest technology and ensure National Grid have energy networks that will meet the future challenges. Be at the heart of one of the greatest engineering challenges facing society; the creation of new sustainable energy solutions for the future.

National Grid is passionate about their "grow their own strategy" and their suite of GCSE to degree level career path development programmes. It's little wonder that they are recognised for excellence and innovation – after all, they have been running some for well over 20 years - so they are some of the best graduates will find anywhere.

GRADUATE VACANCIES IN 2013
ACCOUNTANCY
ENGINEERING
FINANCE
GENERAL MANAGEMENT
IT
LOGISTICS
PROPERTY
PURCHASING
RESEARCH & DEVELOPMENT

NUMBER OF VACANCIES
60+ graduate jobs

LOCATIONS OF VACANCIES

STARTING SALARY FOR 2013
£25,600
£26,600 for those with a Masters.
£2,000 welcome payment.

UNIVERSITY VISITS IN 2012-13
BATH, BRISTOL, CAMBRIDGE, CARDIFF,
IMPERIAL COLLEGE LONDON,
LOUGHBOROUGH, MANCHESTER,
NOTTINGHAM, SHEFFIELD,
SOUTHAMPTON, WARWICK
Please check with your university careers
service for full details of local events.

MINIMUM ENTRY REQUIREMENTS
2.2 Degree
Relevant degree required for some roles.

APPLICATION DEADLINE
31st January 2013

FURTHER INFORMATION
www.Top100GraduateEmployers.com
Register now for the latest news, events
information and graduate recruitment
details for Britain's leading employers.

nationalgrid

Help us keep everyone connected.

Graduate Development Programme – starting salary of £25,600 and £26,600 pa
Student Programmes – starting salaries of £12,500 to £15,600 pa
Engineer Training Programme – starting salary of £23,500 pa
Advanced Apprenticeship Programme – starting salary of £14,950 pa

National Grid's role is to connect people to the energy they use. Society relies on having energy at its finger tips: it is built on it and National Grid owns and manages the systems to which many different energy sources are connected. In Britain we run systems that deliver gas and electricity across the entire country. In the North Eastern states of the US, we provide power directly to millions of customers. Holding a vital position at the centre of the energy system, National Grid join's everything up.

The energy market will dramatically change between now and 2015 and National Grid will play a vital role in connecting new sources of energy generation. The transition to a low carbon economy is set against a background of increasing population, changing economic times and ageing power plants will be unprecedented. This presents individuals with a tremendous opportunity to work with the latest technology and ensure we have energy networks that will meet the future challenges. You can be at the heart of one of the greatest engineering challenges facing society; the creation of new sustainable energy solutions for the future.

At National Grid we're passionate about our "grow our own strategy" and our suite of GCSE to degree level career path development programmes. It's little wonder that they are recognised for excellence and innovation – after all, we've been running some for well over 20 years – so they are some of the best you'll find anywhere.

Please visit our website to find out more and to apply.
**www.nationalgridcareers.com/
Development-Opportunities**

Nestlé is the world's leading nutrition, health and wellness company, employing 330,000 people in over 150 countries, running 461 factories worldwide, generating sales in 2011 of CHF 83.7bn! Brands produced in the UK such as Kit Kat, Buxton, Felix, Nescafé and Shreddies are known worldwide.

With a presence across the world, they have a diverse, truly global environment that brings new perspectives to every challenge and opportunity. As a result, graduates will learn from exceptional people and collaborate across teams, territories and continents because this is a way of life at Nestlé.

The graduate scheme offers unparalleled opportunities to excel and develop a fulfilling career. Graduates are given the chance to contribute every day whilst making an impact long-term, growing as individuals whilst supporting a wider team. Nothing stands still for long at Nestlé, least of all employees who have the vision, desire and ability to grow – as colleagues and as people.

Depending on the scheme, graduates get involved in all aspects of a product's lifecycle from launching the Kit Kat champion campaign, to developing the machinery at the new Buxton factory, to managing the Aero Bubble promotion.

Nestlé's International Development Programme for marketing and sales takes the top graduate talent from markets around the world and moves them onto a scheme offering global opportunities to further develop their core leadership and professional capabilities through exposure to international markets.

Graduates receive a detailed development programme focusing on regular performance evaluation and feedback as they look to perfect those key leadership skills required to be successful as a leader in the business. They also receive cross-functional exposure and work on live projects to deliver real business results. What's more, graduates are in a real job from day one.

GRADUATE VACANCIES IN 2013

ENGINEERING
FINANCE
HUMAN RESOURCES
LOGISTICS
MARKETING
PURCHASING
SALES

NUMBER OF VACANCIES
50 graduate jobs

LOCATIONS OF VACANCIES

STARTING SALARY FOR 2013
£27,000
Plus a £2,000 welcome bonus.

UNIVERSITY VISITS IN 2012-13
ASTON, BATH, BRISTOL, CAMBRIDGE, CARDIFF, DURHAM, EDINBURGH, EXETER, GLASGOW, LANCASTER, LEEDS, LIVERPOOL, LOUGHBOROUGH, MANCHESTER, NEWCASTLE, NOTTINGHAM, OXFORD, SHEFFIELD, STRATHCLYDE, UNIVERSITY COLLEGE LONDON, WARWICK, YORK
Please check with your university careers service for full details of local events.

MINIMUM ENTRY REQUIREMENTS
2.1 Degree
Relevant degree required for some roles.

APPLICATION DEADLINE
Varies by function
Please see website for full details.

FURTHER INFORMATION
www.Top100GraduateEmployers.com
Register now for the latest news, events information and graduate recruitment details for Britain's leading employers.

Good Food, Good Life

I want to create a
better world
and build a better
business

At Nestlé, we encourage our people to grow in more than one dimension, to achieve all they can be both professionally and personally.

Joining Nestlé means you'll be joining a business which combines the freedom to implement locally relevant plans, with the opportunity to call on the global expertise of the world's leading nutrition, health and wellness company. We look to enhance the quality of life everywhere, every day.... creating long-term sustainable value for our consumers, for our communities, and for our shareholders.

At Nestlé there are no limits to your success, if you want it we'll help you get it! Our Academy offers you a lifetime of learning throughout your career offering development and support every step of the way to make sure that you achieve both professional and personal career fulfilment.

The start of your Nestlé Academy journey could be one of our
Graduate Programmes in the following areas:
CPUK (Cereal Partners UK) • Engineering • Finance • HR • Manufacturing & Focused Improvement
Marketing • Quality Assurance • Sales • SHE (Safety, Health & Environment) • Supply Chain
We also offer 12 month placement opportunities as well as Summer Internships.

Find out more about what is out there for you at: http://www.nestlecareers.co.uk

MY WORK *HELPS US WORK.*

AKTHAR HUSSAIN, Electrical Engineering
"The work is dynamic and different, with the chance to create a legacy that will be around forever."

It's natural to associate Network Rail with 'trains and engineering'. In reality, they provide the entire infrastructure and transport network that keeps the country moving. Responsible for tracks, signals, tunnels, bridges, viaducts, level crossings and stations, they touch millions of lives across Britain, every day.

Passenger satisfaction levels are high and they're experiencing record levels of passenger and freight demand. Network Rail's ambition is to continue to meet customer needs, while providing even better value for money in the future.

Investing £35bn on improving the network, they're delivering some of the largest engineering projects that are happening in Europe today. Their graduates are trusted to make a real and valuable contribution from day one. Whether these talented individuals are based in a front-line role or delivering critical support behind the scenes, they help the organisation deliver the railway that's so vital for Britain's economic growth.

After a period of induction, graduates gain experience on a range of placements. While there's plenty of support, it's the graduate that takes control over the pace and content of their progression. There's a vast range of programmes to choose from including: engineering, finance, operations management, project management and information management (IT).

Network Rail see graduates as the future leaders of the organisation, so they take training and development very seriously. Whichever area graduates specialise in, they work towards professional qualifications and receive regular reviews of their performance and development. Every day, they'll see the impact of their fresh-thinking and ambition, as they help Britain work.

GRADUATE VACANCIES IN 2013
ACCOUNTANCY
ENGINEERING
FINANCE
GENERAL MANAGEMENT
IT
LOGISTICS
PROPERTY
PURCHASING

NUMBER OF VACANCIES
100 graduate jobs

LOCATIONS OF VACANCIES

STARTING SALARY FOR 2013
£24,500
Plus a welcome bonus.

UNIVERSITY VISITS IN 2012-13
ASTON, BATH, BRISTOL, CARDIFF, CITY, DURHAM, EDINBURGH, IMPERIAL COLLEGE LONDON, KING'S COLLEGE LONDON, LEEDS, LIVERPOOL, LOUGHBOROUGH, MANCHESTER, NEWCASTLE, NOTTINGHAM, OXFORD, SHEFFIELD, SOUTHAMPTON, STRATHCLYDE, UNIVERSITY COLLEGE LONDON, WARWICK, YORK
Please check with your university careers service for full details of local events.

MINIMUM ENTRY REQUIREMENTS
2.2 Degree

APPLICATION DEADLINE
17th December 2012

FURTHER INFORMATION
www.Top100GraduateEmployers.com
Register now for the latest news, events information and graduate recruitment details for Britain's leading employers.

NATIONAL GRADUATE
DEVELOPMENT PROGRAMME

ngdp.

FOR LOCAL GOVERNMENT

Real life. Real work. Real people.

The ngdp is a two-year graduate management development programme, run by the Local Government Association. The programme was set up to provide local government with the high-calibre managers their communities need – and to give committed graduates the training and opportunities to make a positive impact.

Local government is the largest employer in the UK, with over two million staff in over 400 local authorities and in excess of 500 different occupational areas. Since 2002 approximately 500 graduates have completed the programme, all taking advantage of the wide range of opportunities available with many now holding influential managerial and policy roles. Now is a time of huge change in the public sector and trainees will make a real contribution to bringing these changes about.

The national programme framework is built on a series of placements in key areas within a council and offers a range of experiences and challenges. All of which will provide a broad understanding of different aspects of local government in strategy, front-line service and support. Although employed by a participating authority on a two-year, fixed-term contract, graduates will also benefit from being part of a national programme group, giving them the opportunity to participate in a national induction event, join an established knowledge-sharing network and take part in an accredited series of learning and development components.

The programme has taken graduates in many different directions, with many alumni occupying key roles within the local government and the wider public sector. Ultimately, this is a chance to be part of an exciting period of opportunity and not just propose change, but be the one to make it happen.

GRADUATE VACANCIES IN 2013
GENERAL MANAGEMENT

NUMBER OF VACANCIES
50+ graduate jobs

LOCATIONS OF VACANCIES

STARTING SALARY FOR 2013
£22,958
Plus London weighting.

UNIVERSITY VISITS IN 2012-13
Please check with your university careers service for full details of local events.

MINIMUM ENTRY REQUIREMENTS
2.1 Degree

APPLICATION DEADLINE
Please see website for full details.

FURTHER INFORMATION
www.Top100GraduateEmployers.com
Register now for the latest news, events information and graduate recruitment details for Britain's leading employers.

Local Government Association

NATIONAL GRADUATE DEVELOPMENT PROGRAMME
ngdp
FOR LOCAL GOVERNMENT

Your opportunity to make a difference

"The ngdp is completely unique in terms of the diversity of opportunity it offers and the wide range of skills you can develop. I have had the chance to work with a variety of people - from chief executives and council leaders to binmen and social workers; I have been given real responsibility from day one."

Rosie Barker, Corporate Policy and Research, Oldham Metropolitan Borough Council

"This programme gives you access to the inner workings of local government, a sector that is changing rapidly. There are opportunities for innovation around service delivery and supporting communities. I have been able to work in a number of different departments, delivering a wide array of services which affect people's day to day lives."

Michael Gladstone, Chief Executive's Group, London Borough of Sutton

That's what the ngdp is all about. It's a two-year graduate training programme designed to help you develop as a leader in local government, giving you hands on experience and genuine responsibility. You'll take on a variety of projects. You'll meet all sorts of people. And you'll enjoy all the challenges and opportunities that only come from doing real work.

To find out more about ngdp and why you should join us visit **www.ngdp.org.uk**

www.nhsgraduates.co.uk

graduatescheme@leadershipacademy.nhs.uk

twitter.com/NHSGradscheme   facebook.com/NHSGraduateScheme

Prove yourself

The NHS is like no other organisation on earth. Born out of the ideal that good healthcare should be available to all, it is one of the world's largest publicly funded health services. It has a budget of over £90 billion and employs more than 1 million people. This makes it the single biggest employer in Europe.

The NHS Graduate Management Training Scheme runs every year; lasting up to two years (Finance 2½ years) it has been explicitly designed to create the organisation's future leaders. It consists of four specialisms: Finance Management, General Management, Human Resources Management, and Health Informatics Management. Graduates specialise in one of these areas, acquiring relevant professional qualifications along the way.

Working for the NHS will often mean standing up to high levels of public scrutiny and having decisions closely inspected; graduates will need to be tenacious and resilient and able to respond to an ever changing environment whilst keeping patient care at the heart of what the NHS do.

The Graduate Management Training Scheme offers a fast-track route to a senior leadership role. As such, it's a uniquely demanding experience. To succeed graduates will need the confidence to tackle complex problems head on and the intelligence to contribute new ideas, but above all, the desire to make a difference to patient's lives.

In addition there is also the Healthcare Scientist Training Programme which offers excellent training opportunities within a national postgraduate training programme located in hospitals and health services throughout England. Posts are available within one of three scientific divisions: Life Sciences; Physical Sciences and Biomedical Engineering; and Physiological Sciences.

GRADUATE VACANCIES IN 2013
FINANCE
GENERAL MANAGEMENT
HUMAN RESOURCES
IT

NUMBER OF VACANCIES
Up to 150 graduate jobs

LOCATIONS OF VACANCIES

STARTING SALARY FOR 2013
£Competitive

UNIVERSITY VISITS IN 2012-13
Please check with your university careers service for full details of local events.

MINIMUM ENTRY REQUIREMENTS
2.2 Degree

APPLICATION DEADLINE
Please see website for full details.

FURTHER INFORMATION
www.Top100GraduateEmployers.com
Register now for the latest news, events information and graduate recruitment details for Britain's leading employers.

We'll ask you to justify everything you do.

Starting right here

NHS
Leadership Academy

Graduate Management
Training Scheme

www.nhsgraduates.co.uk

^NORTON ROSE

GRADUATE VACANCIES IN 2013
LAW

NUMBER OF VACANCIES
55 graduate jobs
For training contracts starting in 2015.

LOCATIONS OF VACANCIES

Vacancies also available in Europe, Asia and elsewhere in the world.

STARTING SALARY FOR 2013
£38,000

UNIVERSITY VISITS IN 2012-13
BIRMINGHAM, BRISTOL, CAMBRIDGE,
DURHAM, KING'S COLLEGE LONDON,
LONDON SCHOOL OF ECONOMICS,
NOTTINGHAM, OXFORD, READING,
SHEFFIELD, UNIVERSITY COLLEGE LONDON,
WARWICK, YORK
Please check with your university careers service for full details of local events.

MINIMUM ENTRY REQUIREMENTS
2.1 Degree
AAB at A-Level

APPLICATION DEADLINE
Law: 31st July 2013
Non-Law: 31st April 2013

FURTHER INFORMATION
www.Top100GraduateEmployers.com
Register now for the latest news, events information and graduate recruitment details for Britain's leading employers.

Norton Rose is a leading international legal practice. The firm offers a full business law service to many of the world's pre-eminent financial institutions and corporations from offices in Europe, Asia Pacific, Canada, Africa and the Middle East. Knowing how clients' businesses work and understanding what drives their industries is fundamental to Norton Rose.

Norton Rose lawyers share industry knowledge and sector expertise across borders, enabling them to support clients anywhere in the world. Norton Rose are strong in financial institutions; energy; infrastructure, mining and commodities; transport; technology and innovation; and pharmaceuticals and life sciences.

At Norton Rose it is important that trainees get as much exposure as possible. Successful applicants will therefore experience a varied seat plan, allowing them the widest exposure to different practice areas and international offices in order to enable them to make the best and most informed choice of qualification area. Throughout the training contract, trainees are offered a comprehensive skills training programme to ensure they continue to develop and succeed at every stage in their career. Regular appraisals and reviews ensure trainees are supported during their training contract and beyond.

Norton Rose recruits up to 55 trainee solicitors per year split over two intakes and up to 40 summer vacation scheme students. They look for intelligent, ambitious, internationally focused and commercially-minded individuals to drive their business. The firm recruits trainees who can think creatively and find new ways to solve problems and expect trainees to deliver work that meets the highest professional, ethical and business standards for clients.

NÔRTON ROSE

We are an ambitious, expanding, international legal practice with a clear strategy for the future and a strong industry focus – in financial institutions; energy; infrastructure, mining and commodities; transport; technology and innovation; pharmaceuticals and life sciences.

Can you demonstrate global thinking, commercial acumen and the drive to provide the highest standard of service to clients across these sectors? If so, you'll like our world.

We have offices in Abu Dhabi | Almaty | Amsterdam | Athens | Bahrain | Bangkok | Beijing | Bogotá | Brisbane | Brussels | Calgary | Canberra | Cape Town | Caracas | Casablanca | Dubai | Durban | Frankfurt | Hamburg | Ho Chi Minh City* | Hong Kong | Jakarta* | Johannesburg | London | Melbourne | Milan | Montréal | Moscow | Munich | Ottawa | Paris | Perth | Piraeus | Prague | Québec | Rome | Shanghai | Singapore | Sydney | Tokyo | Toronto | Warsaw *associate office

Our world is demanding, innovative and supportive.
nortonrosegraduates.com

Now more than ever, the nuclear industry is full of opportunities. The organisations that power this fascinating industry are looking for the next generation to help keep pushing the boundaries of technology. nucleargraduates is a unique programme, sponsored by leading companies in the nuclear sector.

Historic power stations are being decommissioned, current power stations are a critical part of the energy mix and a new wave of plants has been given the go ahead. In the defence sector, new and existing submarines provide unique technical and engineering challenges. Nuclear is back on the agenda.

The need for suitably skilled graduates from the UK is greater than ever. Engineers, scientists, environmental specialists, business and commercial minds, talented managers and financial experts will all be essential to the future of this sector. That's why leading businesses and organisations support nucleargraduates.

The nucleargraduates programme is sponsored by more than 20 stakeholders, including Rolls-Royce, Sellafield, Magnox, the Nuclear Decommissioning Authority and International Nuclear Services. All of the companies involved are some of the most innovative and well respected organisations in the nuclear industry.

The unique structure of the nucleargraduates programme means that graduates apply to the sponsoring companies through the nucleargraduates website. Once successful applicants have completed the two-year nucleargraduates programme they are expected to join the sponsor company as a direct entry. Every candidate must apply to a sponsor through the nucleargraduates website.

GRADUATE VACANCIES IN 2013

ENGINEERING

NUMBER OF VACANCIES
45 graduate jobs

LOCATIONS OF VACANCIES

STARTING SALARY FOR 2013
£24,500
Plus a £1,000 Golden Hello.

UNIVERSITY VISITS IN 2012-13
ABERDEEN, ASTON, BATH, BELFAST, BIRMINGHAM, BRISTOL, CAMBRIDGE, CARDIFF, DURHAM, EDINBURGH, EXETER, HULL, IMPERIAL COLLEGE LONDON, LANCASTER, LEEDS, LIVERPOOL, LOUGHBOROUGH, MANCHESTER, NEWCASTLE, NOTTINGHAM, OXFORD, SHEFFIELD, SOUTHAMPTON, STRATHCLYDE, SURREY, WARWICK, YORK
Please check with your university careers service for full details of local events.

MINIMUM ENTRY REQUIREMENTS
2.1 Degree

APPLICATION DEADLINE
December 2012

FURTHER INFORMATION
www.Top100GraduateEmployers.com
Register now for the latest news, events information and graduate recruitment details for Britain's leading employers.

One Nuclear Industry
Hundreds of Opportunities

Decommissioning - Defence - Generation

Three simple steps to achieving expertise in one of the most talked about and least understood industries via nucleargraduates.com:

1 Choose one of the sponsors (Rolls-Royce, Sellafield, Magnox or the NDA)

2 Experience a world class twenty four month long development programme

3 Join your sponsor for a career based on professional excellence and opportunity

nucleargraduates

OLIVER WYMAN

www.oliverwyman.com/careers

facebook.com/OliverWyman **f**   recruitinguk@oliverwyman.com ✉

linkedin.com/company/2454 **in**   twitter.com/OliverWyman **y**

GRADUATE VACANCIES IN 2013

CONSULTING

NUMBER OF VACANCIES
No fixed quota

LOCATIONS OF VACANCIES

STARTING SALARY FOR 2013
£Competitive

UNIVERSITY VISITS IN 2012-13
BATH, BRISTOL, CAMBRIDGE, IMPERIAL
COLLEGE LONDON, LONDON SCHOOL
OF ECONOMICS, OXFORD, UNIVERSITY
COLLEGE LONDON, WARWICK
*Please check with your university careers
service for full details of local events.*

MINIMUM ENTRY REQUIREMENTS
2.1 Degree
340 UCAS points

APPLICATION DEADLINE
1st November 2012
For November 2012 offers.
16th December 2012
For January 2013 offers.

FURTHER INFORMATION
www.Top100GraduateEmployers.com
*Register now for the latest news, events
information and graduate recruitment
details for Britain's leading employers.*

Oliver Wyman is a leading global management consulting firm combining deep industry knowledge with specialised expertise in strategy, operations and risk management. Consultants work alongside clients to develop practical solutions that deliver real impact.

Oliver Wyman offers graduates a highly stimulating work environment, a meaningful professional experience and an opportunity to shape and develop the firm. From day one, consultants are part of a project team, working closely with clients, and are given real responsibility for discrete elements of their work. They will brainstorm and debate with some of the best minds and leaders in the international business world. Consultants are recruited with a view to them becoming Partners of the firm, and a significant proportion of Oliver Wyman's current Partners were elected 6-9 years after joining straight from university.

Reflecting a specialist business model, Oliver Wyman recruits consultants into two tracks. Candidates may apply to either or both Financial Services Management Consulting or General Management Consulting. Oliver Wyman is committed to investing in professional and personal development, and offers unrivalled opportunities for learning with a structured programme of ongoing training throughout a consultant's career. At the same time Oliver Wyman recognises that consulting is an apprenticeship, and nothing can beat high quality 'on the job learning'.

Outstanding students of any discipline are welcome to apply although strong analytical skills and a passion for applying them to real world problem-solving are a must. Successful candidates will combine intellectual curiosity and self-confidence with entrepreneurship and a desire to contribute fully to shaping the firm's future.

Oxfam
Be Humankind

www.oxfam.org.uk/interns

Swimming, cinema and socialising with friends...

Few organisations offer such a unique opportunity to contribute towards overcoming poverty and suffering. Oxfam has been fighting it for 70 years and graduates can be part of it. Poverty isn't inevitable, so Oxfam gives people what they need to fight it.

Oxfam is one of the most experienced development agencies in the world, working in more than 70 countries. It has run its Voluntary Internship scheme since 2006 and has helped to provide valuable experience and skills to hundreds of people. Voluntary Internships provide a structured, time-bound opportunity, so that graduates can get the most out of volunteering.

Oxfam's Voluntary Internships are based on projects where its people are able to contribute and add significant value to an area of the organisation. Voluntary Internships are usually between 3 and 7 months, depending on the project. Oxfam pays local travel and lunch expenses so that its volunteers aren't out of pocket whilst volunteering.

The roles could be in Oxfam's Oxford Headquarters, a shop or a regional office. They range from Voluntary Assistant Shop Managers, to Marketing & Communications Assistants working in Oxfam's Community Fundraising team, to HR & Recruitment Advisors, to Research Executives in the Campaigns Division. Regardless of whether graduates want to plan a fundraising event, work on a campaign project, or help to run a shop, they will get to experience how a major international Non Government Organisation works and enjoy a friendly, open and passionate working environment.

Voluntary Internships are a great way to learn new skills, experience how a large NGO operates and help to contribute towards Oxfam's goal of overcoming poverty and suffering around the world.

...wouldn't you rather put 'saving the world' on your CV?

Voluntary Internship Opportunities | UK-wide

Right wrongs right here. Take up an internship with an organisation that won't stand for climate change, poverty or injustice – and stand out. Swing into action at **www.oxfam.org.uk/interns**

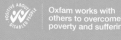
 Oxfam

Be Humankind

www.penguin.co.uk

hr@uk.penguingroup.com ✉

Pop-up

Allen Lane introduced the first Penguin paperback over 75 years ago, with the intention of bringing intelligent books to the public at a low price. Since then, the paperback list has developed enormously, and Penguin has become the most recognisable brand name in publishing.

Penguin publishes some of the world's finest authors, from Antony Beevor to Zadie Smith (with such brilliant writers as Jamie Oliver, Malcolm Gladwell, Niall Ferguson, Roald Dahl and Marian Keyes in between, to name but a few). Penguin is also home to DK, Rough Guides, Puffin and Ladybird. In short, it is obsessed with books and stories.

Penguin is fanatical about the quality of what it produces, and the professionalism with which it goes about business. It wants to be brave, imaginative and decent in everything it does. Penguin publishes new kinds of content, on new platforms for new audiences. And it still manufactures millions of that cherished, centuries-old artefact: the book.

Penguin has a variety of roles across the business for publicists, production controllers, marketers, designers, accountants, sales, rights and operations people as well as the traditional editorial and publishing roles.

Penguin has recently launched a new paid internship scheme and will welcome the first intake of interns to the business this summer. The internship programme lasts for 10 weeks, and each intern is placed in a specific part of the business where they will take on a particular, meaningful project – i.e. they won't be making the tea and fetching the post!

This is the perfect opportunity for anyone looking to get an insight into a dynamic industry with a brand that not only has a rich heritage but is always looking forward.

GRADUATE VACANCIES IN 2013

ACCOUNTANCY
FINANCE
HUMAN RESOURCES
LAW
LOGISTICS
MARKETING
MEDIA
SALES

NUMBER OF VACANCIES
Around 30-50 graduate jobs

LOCATIONS OF VACANCIES

STARTING SALARY FOR 2013
£21,656

UNIVERSITY VISITS IN 2012-13
ASTON, BIRMINGHAM, BRISTOL, DURHAM, IMPERIAL COLLEGE LONDON, LEEDS, LONDON SCHOOL OF ECONOMICS, SCHOOL OF AFRICAN STUDIES, WARWICK, YORK
Please check with your university careers service for full details of local events.

APPLICATION DEADLINE
Year-round recruitment

FURTHER INFORMATION
www.Top100GraduateEmployers.com
Register now for the latest news, events information and graduate recruitment details for Britain's leading employers.

REASONS TO
BECOME A PENGUIN

1) You get to work with your favourite authors and some of the biggest brands in publishing. What could be more fun than that? **2) Our award-winning output.** Over the past year, we have won plaudits for everything from our children's books to our iPad apps. We don't like to boast, but the trophy cabinet is always pretty full. **3) Penguin is the best-loved publisher.** We have been around for over 75 years and we're still inspiring the world with stories. **4) We're a diverse bunch.** And we think publishing should be for everyone. **5) Penguin leads the digital charge.** Check out our array of apps and eBooks. Visit penguin.co.uk or follow us on Twitter. Find us on Facebook or Pinterest or read our blogs. We're always looking for new ideas and new ways of doing things. **6) People pay attention to what we do.** They just do. They can't help it. **7) We think that Penguin is a special breed of bird.** We believe Penguin matters. The books and digital products we publish enrich the lives of millions of readers around the world. They make people laugh, cry, think – and everything in between.

 8) You never need to explain what your company does at parties. When you say 'I work for Penguin', everyone gets just a little bit jealous. **9) We're good and green.** Staff are entitled to three charity days every year and have their fundraising matched by Penguin. We ranked No. 7 in The Sunday Times Green List. We even have our own Penguin wood. **10) We're the only publishing company in here.** Go on, check. See?

P&G

> " You lead from
> day one at P&G.
> The training is
> phenomenal. "
>
> Jenna Leathers, Gillette

P&G | ⬤⬤⬤⬤⬤
WORLDWIDE PARTNER

GRADUATE VACANCIES IN 2013

- ACCOUNTANCY
- ENGINEERING
- FINANCE
- HUMAN RESOURCES
- IT
- LOGISTICS
- MARKETING
- RESEARCH & DEVELOPMENT
- SALES

NUMBER OF VACANCIES
100 graduate jobs

LOCATIONS OF VACANCIES

Vacancies also available elsewhere in the world.

STARTING SALARY FOR 2013
£28,600-£31,000
Plus a benefits package.

UNIVERSITY VISITS IN 2012-13
ASTON, BATH, BIRMINGHAM, BRISTOL, CAMBRIDGE, DURHAM, EDINBURGH, IMPERIAL COLLEGE LONDON, KING'S COLLEGE LONDON, LANCASTER, LEEDS, LONDON SCHOOL OF ECONOMICS, MANCHESTER, NOTTINGHAM, OXFORD, SHEFFIELD, STRATHCLYDE, TRINITY COLLEGE DUBLIN, UNIVERSITY COLLEGE DUBLIN, WARWICK
Please check with your university careers service for full details of local events.

MINIMUM ENTRY REQUIREMENTS
Relevant degree required for some roles.

APPLICATION DEADLINE
Year-round recruitment
Early application advised.

FURTHER INFORMATION
www.Top100GraduateEmployers.com
Register now for the latest news, events information and graduate recruitment details for Britain's leading employers.

Four billion times a day, P&G brands touch the lives of people around the world. They reach those who shave with a Gillette Fusion ProGlide or Venus razor, who wash their hair with Pantene or Head & Shoulders, who wear a scent from Hugo Boss, those who wash their clothes with Ariel (to name but a few of the nearly 300 brands around the globe).

The company has one of the strongest portfolios of trusted, leading quality brands, including Pampers, Ariel, Always, Pantene, Gillette, Fairy, Lenor, Iams, Crest, Oral-B, Duracell, Olay, Head & Shoulders, Wella and Braun. The P&G community consists of around 127,000 employees working in over 80 countries worldwide.

P&G attracts and recruits the finest people in the world, because they develop talents almost exclusively from within. This means graduates won't just get their first job out of university, they are being hired with the expectation that they will grow into one of P&G's future leaders. Maybe even the next CEO. New starters with P&G can expect a job with responsibility from day one and a career with a variety of challenging roles that develop and broaden their skills, together with the support of training and coaching to help them succeed.

P&G look for more than just good academic records from their applicants. They are looking for graduates who are smart and savvy, leaders who stand out from the crowd, who are able to get things done. They want to hear about achievements at work, in clubs, societies, voluntary and community activities and to see how graduates have stretched and challenged themselves and others. Most functions within the company welcome applicants from any degree discipline. Product Supply requires an engineering degree and R&D requires an engineering or science degree.

We develop the world's best.

How long before it's you?
Secure a career at www.*PG*careers.com

pwc

www.pwc.com/uk/careers

facebook.com/PwCCareersUK

youtube.com/careerspwc twitter.com/PwC_UK_Careers

Nabeel, More London Office

Opportunities are at the heart of a career with PwC. Opportunities to grow as an individual, to build lasting relationships and make an impact in a place where people, quality and value mean everything. A career at PwC means to be a part of the world's leading professional services network and enjoy the benefits that come with that.

Work directly with big name clients and get to grips with the value they're looking for by getting into the detail. PwC provides an environment to explore new opportunities and to help graduates grow whilst providing the best learning and development around.

No matter what year undergraduates are in at University, there are many ways they can learn more about the firm and where their skills, interests and career goals would best fit, on one of PwC's work experience programmes.

For graduates, whichever area of the business they choose to join, and there are many to choose from, all routes offer the same deal. They'll learn, discover, develop and make a difference through the work they do, and the experiences they have.

PwC chooses the best people to work with them, from a wide range of backgrounds and degree subjects. As well as academic excellence, they need graduates who can build and maintain relationships, put themselves in others' shoes, and make a positive impact on the firm, their clients and each other.

For graduates looking for a rewarding career in business, the opportunity to work towards a professional qualification and unparalleled support in training and development - then they need to join PwC. They're focused on helping graduates reach their full potential whilst providing a competitive salary and personally tailored benefits package.

GRADUATE VACANCIES IN 2013

ACCOUNTANCY
CONSULTING
FINANCE
IT
LAW

NUMBER OF VACANCIES
Around 1,200 graduate jobs

LOCATIONS OF VACANCIES

STARTING SALARY FOR 2013
£Competitive

UNIVERSITY VISITS IN 2012-13
ABERDEEN, ASTON, BATH, BELFAST, BIRMINGHAM, BRISTOL, BRUNEL, CAMBRIDGE, CARDIFF, DURHAM, EAST ANGLIA, EDINBURGH, EXETER, GLASGOW, HERIOT-WATT, HULL, IMPERIAL COLLEGE LONDON, KING'S COLLEGE LONDON, LANCASTER, LEEDS, LIVERPOOL, LONDON SCHOOL OF ECONOMICS, LOUGHBOROUGH, MANCHESTER, NEWCASTLE, NOTTINGHAM, OXFORD, PLYMOUTH, READING, SHEFFIELD, SOUTHAMPTON, ST ANDREWS, STRATHCLYDE, SWANSEA, UNIVERSITY COLLEGE LONDON, WARWICK, YORK
Please check with your university careers service for full details of local events.

MINIMUM ENTRY REQUIREMENTS
2.1 Degree
300 UCAS points

APPLICATION DEADLINE
Varies by function

FURTHER INFORMATION
www.Top100GraduateEmployers.com
Register now for the latest news, events information and graduate recruitment details for Britain's leading employers.

The experience stays with you

Stephanie at a fashion retailer

Assurance
Actuarial
Consulting
Financial Advisory
Tax
Technology

All degree disciplines,
2:1 or above.
300+ UCAS tariff
or equivalent.

---

*Voted employer of
choice by students
in The Times Top 100
Graduate Employers
Survey for nine
years running.*

Opportunities with the UK's number one graduate employer

Offices across the UK » Join Spring, Summer or Autumn

Your career is just that, yours. You choose it. You live it. You make it happen. To get the best from it, you need the best opportunities. That's why opportunity is at the heart of a career with us. Opportunities to grow as an individual, to build lasting relationships and make an impact in a place where people, quality and value mean everything. For Stephanie, this means working with a leading online fashion retailer. And having spent lots of time working at their offices to give them the support they really value, she now understands how their business revolves around the seasons, not just the financial year-end. Join PwC – we're focused on helping you reach your full potential.

It's the opportunity of a lifetime.

www.pwc.com/uk/careers

www.facebook.com/PwCCareersUK

pwc

WE LIKE THE WAY YOU THINK

Rolls-Royce's technology has underpinned some of the most spectacular achievements on land, at sea and in the air. Now a global company active in 50 countries, the firm looks to have an even more exciting future. With an order book currently standing at over £60 billion, Rolls-Royce expects to double in size over the next decade.

For graduates, that means a wealth of opportunities: to work with some of the world's finest professional minds; to play a part in the future of responsible, low-impact power systems; to develop their skills and expertise within a world-class environment; and to gain international exposure with a company known the world over for excellence, reliability and integrity.

The company is able to attract excellent people because of the specialist skills and knowledge that can be taught to the highest levels. Graduates are able to join all sorts of areas, from engineering and commercial to HR and finance, and can choose from two graduate programmes. The Professional Excellence Programme teaches the skills needed to be an expert in a chosen field, allowing graduates to learn directly from some of the industry's most experienced professionals. The Leadership Development Programme helps grow the future leaders of the business and will channel learning in a broader business context, tackling the operational and managerial dimensions of the chosen discipline.

Who are they looking for? There's a certain mindset that's shared by all Rolls-Royce people. A relentless desire to make things work better and to redefine the standards everyone else lives by. Whatever the role, successful applicants will need to show the same passion and collaborative spirit that's underpinned the company's greatest achievements over the last hundred years.

GRADUATE VACANCIES IN 2013

ENGINEERING
FINANCE
GENERAL MANAGEMENT
HUMAN RESOURCES
PURCHASING

NUMBER OF VACANCIES
400 graduate jobs

LOCATIONS OF VACANCIES

Vacancies also available in Europe, the USA, Asia and elsewhere in the world.

STARTING SALARY FOR 2013
£26,300-£28,800
Plus a £2,000 joining bonus.

UNIVERSITY VISITS IN 2012-13
BATH, BRISTOL, CAMBRIDGE, EDINBURGH, EXETER, IMPERIAL COLLEGE LONDON, LONDON SCHOOL OF ECONOMICS, LOUGHBOROUGH, MANCHESTER, NOTTINGHAM, OXFORD, SOUTHAMPTON, STRATHCLYDE, WARWICK
Please check with your university careers service for full details of local events.

MINIMUM ENTRY REQUIREMENTS
2.1 Degree

APPLICATION DEADLINE
Year-round recruitment
Early application advised.

FURTHER INFORMATION
www.Top100GraduateEmployers.com
Register now for the latest news, events information and graduate recruitment details for Britain's leading employers.

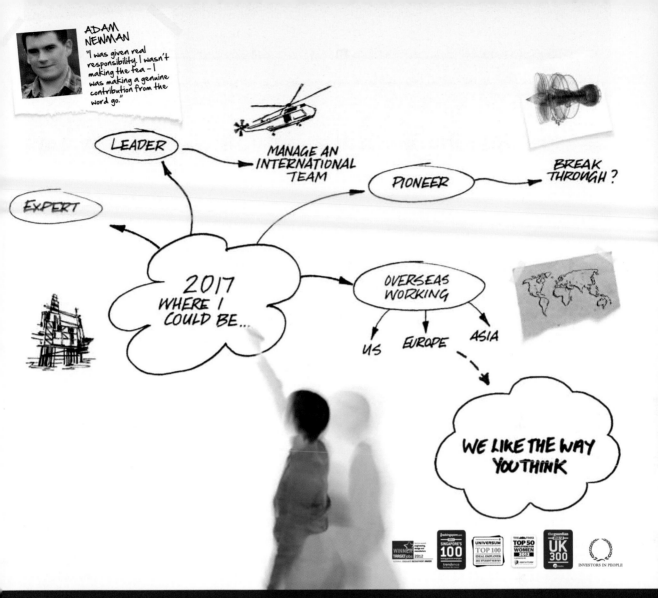

Graduate opportunities

Rolls-Royce has a reputation for big ideas. We're known the world over for high-performance engineering and innovative technologies. We have enabled land-speed records, designed ships that can shatter sheets of Arctic ice, and built turbines that generate power wherever the world needs it. And behind all of our success, you'll find brilliant thinking from some of the sharpest minds around. So if you have big ideas of your own, this could be the perfect place for you to turn them into reality, with our first-class training and mentoring.

We have many opportunities for talented graduates from almost every discipline, across programmes in Commercial, Customer Management, Engineering, Finance, Health, Safety & Environment, Human Resources, Manufacturing Engineering, Operations Management, Programme Management, Purchasing and Supply Chain Planning & Control.

www.rolls-royce.com/graduates

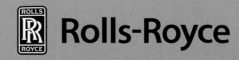

GRADUATE VACANCIES IN 2013

ENGINEERING

GENERAL MANAGEMENT

HUMAN RESOURCES

IT

LOGISTICS

NUMBER OF VACANCIES
130+ graduate jobs

LOCATIONS OF VACANCIES

With hundreds of aircraft and more than 30,000 active personnel, the Royal Air Force (RAF) is a key part of the British Armed Forces, defending the UK and its interests, strengthening international peace and stability, as well as being a force for good in the world.

People lie at the heart of the RAF and it relies upon their professionalism, dedication and courage to achieve the RAF's vision of being 'an agile, adaptable and capable Air Force that, person for person, is second to none, and that makes a decisive air power contribution in support of the UK Defence Mission'.

The world is a changing place and so is the Royal Air Force; it is becoming a smaller, more dynamic and more flexible force able to carry out its missions. To meet the changing times and challenges, and because of the greater capability of technology, the number of people in the RAF has reduced in recent years.

However, this allows the RAF to focus on the staff they have and ensure that they get the very best equipment and training. Recruiting people of the right quality is therefore a key part of the RAF's vision for the future.

The RAF encompasses all aspects of operations, including the use of the very latest hi-tech equipment but the centre of the RAF's vision has always been its people – and it always will be. It prides itself on attracting the highest quality recruits from all sectors of society and provides first-class training and continuing development.

Officers in the Royal Air Force are expected to lead from the front, setting standards for the men and women under their command. For graduates, there are more than twenty different roles to chose from including Air Traffic Control Officer and Logistics or Flight Operations Officer, as well as opportunities for qualified doctors, nurses and dentists.

STARTING SALARY FOR 2013
£29,500
Salary on completion of basic training.

UNIVERSITY VISITS IN 2012-13
Please check with your university careers service for full details of local events.

MINIMUM ENTRY REQUIREMENTS
5 GCSEs, 2 A-Levels
Relevant degree required for some roles.

APPLICATION DEADLINE
Year-round recruitment
Early application is advised.

FURTHER INFORMATION
www.Top100GraduateEmployers.com
Register now for the latest news, events information and graduate recruitment details for Britain's leading employers.

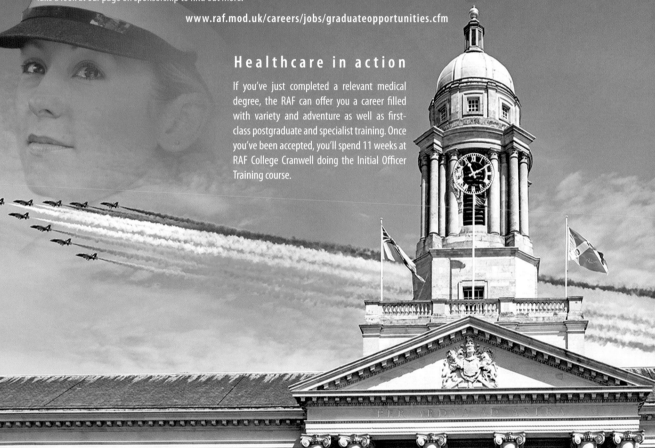

RBS is a global financial services group operating in the UK, Europe, the Americas and Asia Pacific. As the organisation moves forward, graduates will have a real opportunity to shape the future direction of RBS, helping to build a safer and stronger bank.

In return, graduates can develop a career that both challenges and rewards them. As well as world-class training and development programmes, they will enjoy exposure to different areas across the business and early responsibility. At every stage, graduates will have the support of a strong network of managers and mentors. There are also opportunities to build relationships outside of work too, through a wide variety of educational, social and CSR initiatives.

RBS is much more concerned with who graduates are than what they've studied. The organisation is filled with people who have degrees in everything from Russian Literature and Photography to Agricultural Studies and Engineering. Whatever they studied RBS graduates all have certain traits in common: a passion for finance, the ability to learn quickly, plenty of drive and enthusiasm, and the ambition to succeed in a competitive and constantly changing industry.

If graduates have a strong academic record and can demonstrate the right qualities, RBS will develop their existing skills and knowledge to help them reach their full potential.

RBS has a wide range of graduate and internship programmes, from technical roles in markets and risk to leadership roles in operations and business services. Each focuses on a different area of RBS's business and will allow graduates to contribute in their own individual way.

GRADUATE VACANCIES IN 2013

ACCOUNTANCY

FINANCE

GENERAL MANAGEMENT

INVESTMENT BANKING

IT

NUMBER OF VACANCIES
500+ graduate jobs

LOCATIONS OF VACANCIES

Vacancies also available in Europe, the USA, Asia and elsewhere in the world.

STARTING SALARY FOR 2013
£Competitive

UNIVERSITY VISITS IN 2012-13
BIRMINGHAM, BRISTOL, CAMBRIDGE, DURHAM, EDINBURGH, IMPERIAL COLLEGE LONDON, LONDON SCHOOL OF ECONOMICS, MANCHESTER, NOTTINGHAM, OXFORD, SHEFFIELD, UNIVERSITY COLLEGE LONDON, WARWICK
Please check with your university careers service for full details of local events.

MINIMUM ENTRY REQUIREMENTS
2.1 Degree

APPLICATION DEADLINE
Varies by function

FURTHER INFORMATION
www.Top100GraduateEmployers.com
Register now for the latest news, events information and graduate recruitment details for Britain's leading employers.

RBS Group

The progress you make.
The bank you build.

The fresh-thinking you generate. The conversations you instigate. The skills you develop. The relationships you grow. As a graduate here at RBS, the unique contribution you make will help shape the future of our organisation. You'll need to be able to work in a constantly changing environment and there will be plenty of challenges along the way - but, in return, you can expect to build a truly rewarding career.

Ready to make a lasting difference?

Visit **rbsbankyoubuild.com** for more.

www.royalnavy.mod.uk/careers

twitter.com/RoyalNavy facebook.com/RoyalNavyRecruitment

Throughout the course of history, a life at sea has always attracted those with a taste for travel and adventure. But in today's unpredictable job market, there are now plenty of other reasons for graduates and final-year students to consider a challenging and wide-ranging career with the Royal Navy.

The Royal Navy is, first and foremost, a fighting force, serving alongside Britain's allies in conflicts around the world. It also protects UK ports, fishing grounds and merchant ships, helping to combat international smuggling, terrorism and piracy. Increasingly, its 35,000 personnel are involved in humanitarian and relief missions, where their skills, discipline and resourcefulness make a real difference to people's lives.

Graduates are able to join the Royal Navy as Officers – the senior leadership and management team in the various branches, which range from Engineering and Warfare to Medical, the Fleet Air Arm and Logistics. Starting salaries of at least £29,587 compare well with those in industry, with additional pay available for some branches including the Submarine Service and Fleet Air Arm.

Those wanting to join the Royal Navy as an Engineer – either Marine, Weapon or Engineer Officer, above or below the water (traditionally men only for the submarine service; women will serve on submarines for the first time by the end of 2013) – could work on anything from sensitive electronics to massive gas-turbine engines and nuclear weapons. What's more, the Royal Navy can offer a secure, flexible career with the potential to extend to age 50.

The opportunities for early responsibility, career development, sport, recreation and travel exceed any in civilian life. With its global reach and responsibilities, the Royal Navy still offers the chance to see the world, while pursuing a challenging, varied and fulfilling career.

GRADUATE VACANCIES IN 2013

ENGINEERING

FINANCE

GENERAL MANAGEMENT

HUMAN RESOURCES

IT

LAW

LOGISTICS

RESEARCH & DEVELOPMENT

NUMBER OF VACANCIES
No fixed quota

LOCATIONS OF VACANCIES

Vacancies also available elsewhere in the world.

STARTING SALARY FOR 2013
£29,587

UNIVERSITY VISITS IN 2012-13
ABERDEEN, ASTON, BATH, BELFAST, BIRMINGHAM, BRISTOL, BRUNEL, CARDIFF, DUNDEE, DURHAM, EAST ANGLIA, EDINBURGH, EXETER, HERIOT-WATT, LEEDS, LEICESTER, LIVERPOOL, LOUGHBOROUGH, MANCHESTER, NEWCASTLE, PLYMOUTH, SHEFFIELD, ULSTER, UNIVERSITY COLLEGE LONDON, YORK
Please check with your university careers service for full details of local events.

MINIMUM ENTRY REQUIREMENTS
Relevant degree required for some roles.

APPLICATION DEADLINE
Year-round recruitment

FURTHER INFORMATION
www.Top100GraduateEmployers.com
Register now for the latest news, events information and graduate recruitment details for Britain's leading employers.

YOU MANOEUVRE A WARSHIP NOT STRUGGLE FOR A PARKING SPACE

ROYAL NAVY OFFICER

Being an officer in the Royal Navy is a career like any other, but the circumstances and places are sometimes extraordinary. With opportunities ranging from Engineer Officer to Medical Officer, it's a responsible, challenging career that will take you further than you've been before. If you want more than just a job, join the Royal Navy and live a life without limits.

LIFE WITHOUT LIMITS
08456 07 55 55
ROYALNAVY.MOD.UK/CAREERS

Sainsbury's

Sainsbury's is a retailer with a great heritage and a clear purposeful vision for the future. With 22 million shoppers every week, that's a 16.6 percent market share with over 30,000 products, over 1,000 stores across the UK and more than 150,000 employees.

As the oldest and one of the largest food businesses in the country, they strive to deliver an ever-improving shopping experience for their customers. The numbers above prove that they have something special at Sainsbury's – a place that has become not just a great place to shop, but also a business that's a great place to work. They are an established brand, based around trust, quality and loyalty which has created the perfect platform from which to explore new product ranges, enter new markets and develop their online offering.

Sainsbury's has always led the retail field. But the more they extend their brand into new areas, the stronger the bonds with their customers need to be. To achieve this, they need 2020 leaders: individuals with outstanding intellect, business acumen and ambition. Not graduates who want to grow with them, but natural pacesetters who expect, demand and deserve senior responsibility very early in their careers. Sainsbury's realise that this type of person is rare; but they offer the rewards, the challenges and the opportunities to attract them.

The Sainsbury's 2020 Leaders Programme is specifically designed to accelerate a small group of high calibre graduates through to the top of the organisation, giving them the necessary skills to influence and deliver in any business area. Graduates can join the 2020 Leaders Programme on one of the three streams Commercial, People and Operations, depending on their interests and how they see their career developing in the future. This is a unique development opportunity for graduates who can demonstrate outstanding leadership.

GRADUATE VACANCIES IN 2013
HUMAN RESOURCES
LOGISTICS
MARKETING
PURCHASING
RETAILING

NUMBER OF VACANCIES
20 graduate jobs

LOCATIONS OF VACANCIES

STARTING SALARY FOR 2013
£32,000
Plus an annual bonus based on both business and personal performance.

UNIVERSITY VISITS IN 2012-13
BATH, BIRMINGHAM, BRISTOL, CAMBRIDGE, DURHAM, EDINBURGH, LEEDS, MANCHESTER, NOTTINGHAM, OXFORD, UNIVERSITY COLLEGE LONDON, WARWICK
Please check with your university careers service for full details of local events.

MINIMUM ENTRY REQUIREMENTS
2.1 Degree
ABB at A-Level
Plus B in GCSE Maths and English.

APPLICATION DEADLINE
Late November 2012
Early application advised.

FURTHER INFORMATION
www.Top100GraduateEmployers.com
Register now for the latest news, events information and graduate recruitment details for Britain's leading employers.

2020 leaders stand out

Then they
move up.

The 2020 Leaders Programme
Very Competitive Starting Salary

sainsburys.jobs/graduates

 **Santander**

Santander UK plc is one of the UK's leading personal financial services companies and one of its largest providers of mortgages and savings products, with some 25 million customers, an extensive branch network, over 24,000 employees and more than 1.6 million UK shareholders.

There is a strong emphasis within Santander UK to change the focus of the retail bank to customers from products. They are also growing the SME business through a combination of new business and its integration with The Royal Bank of Scotland. The aim is to make Santander UK the 'SME Bank of Choice' and in doing so they will continue to diversify their overall business mix. A third key focus is on continued IT investment and efficiency, with £490 million of planned investment over three years and continued improvements in customer service.

There continues to be an increasing appetite to recruit exceptional talent into Santander UK in order to help build a strong pipeline of future leaders. The graduate programme has been designed to provide the right candidates with a thorough and solid grounding to allow them to kick-start their career within Santander and their chosen business area. Santander's graduate programmes are normally offered in Audit, Santander Corporate, Commercial and Business Banking, Finance, Global Banking and Markets, HR, Marketing, Operations, Retail Banking and Telephone Distribution.

In addition to having a high level of responsibility from day one and the frequent opportunity to get involved in essential networking, CSR and business events, graduates will receive the knowledge and experience needed to realise their full potential. As long as they demonstrate the required level of skills and behaviours and have the passion and enthusiasm to succeed, then Santander UK is the perfect company to develop their career with.

GRADUATE VACANCIES IN 2013
FINANCE
GENERAL MANAGEMENT
RETAILING

NUMBER OF VACANCIES
115 graduate jobs

LOCATIONS OF VACANCIES

STARTING SALARY FOR 2013
£22,000-£26,000
*Mobility Allowance paid
(subject to scheme).*

UNIVERSITY VISITS IN 2012-13
ABERDEEN, ASTON, BATH, BIRMINGHAM, BRADFORD, EXETER, IMPERIAL COLLEGE LONDON, LANCASTER, LEEDS, LEICESTER, LIVERPOOL, LONDON SCHOOL OF ECONOMICS, LOUGHBOROUGH, MANCHESTER, NEWCASTLE, NOTTINGHAM, SHEFFIELD, UNIVERSITY COLLEGE LONDON, WARWICK
Please check with your university careers service for full details of local events.

MINIMUM ENTRY REQUIREMENTS
2.1 Degree
280 UCAS points

APPLICATION DEADLINE
Year-round recruitment
Early application advised.

FURTHER INFORMATION
www.Top100GraduateEmployers.com
Register now for the latest news, events information and graduate recruitment details for Britain's leading employers.

www.savills.co.uk/graduate

gradrecruitment@savills.com

twitter.com/careersinpropRT 🐦 www.savills.co.uk/facebookgradcareers **f**

Savills UK is a leading global real estate service provider listed on the London Stock Exchange. The company employs over 20,000 staff and has 500 offices and associates worldwide, providing all trainees with excellent scope for international experience as their careers develop.

Savills passionately believe their graduates are future leaders and as such make a huge investment in them. Savills graduates are given responsibility from day one, in teams who highly value their contribution, allowing them to be involved in some of the world's most high-profile property deals and developments. Graduates are surrounded by expert professionals and experienced team members from whom they learn and seek advice. Individual achievement is rewarded and Savills look for bold graduates with entrepreneurial flair.

This year Savills are proud to be The Times Graduate Employer of Choice for Property for the sixth consecutive year and have been the TARGETjobs National Graduate Recruitment Awards' "Most Popular Graduate Recruiter in Property" in 2009, 2010 & 2011. Great work life balance, structured training and a dynamic working environment are amongst the factors which see Savills nominated by final year students as an the preferred property employer year on year.

The Savills graduate programme offers the chance to gain an internationally recognised Professional qualification. Offering roles within Surveying, Planning and Estate Agency, over half of Savills graduate programme vacancies are for positions outside of London. Offices in exciting locations around the UK work with high-profile and important clients. The diversity of Savills services means there is the flexibility to carve out a fulfilling, individual and self-tailored career path regardless of the location.

Think of a career in property **think Savills**

At Savills the opportunities come thick and fast – and we want you to grab them. You'll gain a Professional qualification and will have the potential to move between sectors and departments to make your career path your own. And because we reward talent and ability, there's no limit to what you can achieve.

savills

savills.co.uk/graduates

Shell is a global group of energy and petrochemicals companies with far-reaching business interests – from oil exploration to power generation to consumer services. They play a key role in helping to meet the world's growing demand for energy in economically, environmentally and socially responsible ways.

Shell considers their global graduate programmes to be the training schemes for the next generation of senior leaders so in the UK they recruit only around 150 of the highest potential, carefully selected graduates and postgraduates each year. Meeting the world's energy challenges isn't going to be easy so of course they need people who excel both intellectually and personally, but in return they offer some of the highest financial and personal rewards available to graduates.

Successful applicants will be placed into one of a diverse range of programmes across Shell's business depending on their aspirations and the needs of the business. Typically opportunities arise in fields such as IT, Finance, HR, Trading, Sales & Marketing, Supply & Distribution and, of course, Engineering.

Each graduate programme provides an average of 3 years of on-the-job development in real roles within the business. In each chosen field graduates will have the chance to complete three placements giving them a diverse range experience designed to ensure they have the skills and experience needed to move swiftly into a senior management position. From day one they may be managing high impact projects, people and/or considerable budgets.

Graduate starters will get a mentor and 'buddy' to support them and the training and development to enable them to maximise their potential. Professional qualifications such as CIMA, ACCA, CIPD and CIM are fully supported. The application process for Shell's graduate programmes is rigorous, but is designed to enable the most talented graduates to stand out.

GRADUATE VACANCIES IN 2013
ENGINEERING
FINANCE
HUMAN RESOURCES
IT
LOGISTICS
MARKETING
PURCHASING
RESEARCH & DEVELOPMENT
SALES

NUMBER OF VACANCIES
100+ graduate jobs

LOCATIONS OF VACANCIES

Vacancies also available in Europe, the USA, Asia and elsewhere in the world.

STARTING SALARY FOR 2013
£32,500+
For UK roles. Various reward packages dependent on base location.

UNIVERSITY VISITS IN 2012-13
ABERDEEN, BATH, CAMBRIDGE, HERIOT-WATT, IMPERIAL COLLEGE LONDON, LEEDS, LONDON SCHOOL OF ECONOMICS, MANCHESTER, OXFORD, SHEFFIELD, STRATHCLYDE, WARWICK
Please check with your university careers service for full details of local events.

APPLICATION DEADLINE
Year-round recruitment
Early application advised.

FURTHER INFORMATION
www.Top100GraduateEmployers.com
Register now for the latest news, events information and graduate recruitment details for Britain's leading employers.

WE FOUND A WAY TO GET HIM TO MARKET. THINK HOW FAR WE COULD TAKE YOU.

GRADUATES WANTED

As a Graduate with Shell, you'll play an integral part in creating better energy solutions, right from the very start of your career. Solutions like Shell Instapave, a road surface designed to seal rural gravel roads, giving access to vital economic services, like the local market. This is just one example of where you could contribute and develop your skills. With on-the-job training and excellent rewards, you'll have the opportunity to define your career in an innovative and challenging environment.

To find out where you fit in visit **www.shell.com/careers**

Let's deliver better energy solutions together.

Shell is an equal opportunity employer.

sky

Over 20 years ago, Sky started out as a satellite TV broadcaster. Through imagination, innovation, and with customers at the heart of everything it does, Sky now leads the industry, combining award winning technology and the best entertainment to excite and inspire over 10 million customers.

Sky is a company with a history of firsts: the first integrated set-top box and digital video recorder (Sky+), the UK's first HD TV service and the world's first live 3D TV sports event. Sky is the UK's fastest growing broadband and talk provider, with its rapidly expanding portfolio of home communications products, betting and gaming services, as well as being a UK leader in app development, it's easy to see Sky are paving the way in broadcasting, technology and entertainment.

Recently, Sky launched a dedicated F1 channel, Sky News Arabia, plus a new Internet TV service, Now TV. Sky continue to commission an increasing number of British programmes in order to bring customers the best in fresh new home grown shows and this is a chance to be part of an exciting future.

This is all delivered across an ever increasing range of innovative platforms like Sky Go, one of many Sky apps developed for multimedia platforms such as iPad and Xbox to enhance the customer's entertainment.

Sky believes in better and so do their graduates. The entrepreneurial spirit makes sure that Sky never stands still. Neither will those who join, with Sky looking for graduates with ambition, initiative and confidence to take responsibility from the start. Whatever area of the business graduates join, Sky promises excellent training, great exposure and a fun, fast moving start to working life. There's also funding towards qualifications in graduates' chosen business area.

GRADUATE VACANCIES IN 2013

ACCOUNTANCY
CONSULTING
FINANCE
GENERAL MANAGEMENT
HUMAN RESOURCES
IT
LOGISTICS
MARKETING
MEDIA
PURCHASING

NUMBER OF VACANCIES
100 graduate jobs

LOCATIONS OF VACANCIES

STARTING SALARY FOR 2013
£22,000-£30,000

UNIVERSITY VISITS IN 2012-13
ASTON, BATH, BRISTOL, BRUNEL, CAMBRIDGE, DURHAM, EDINBURGH, HERIOT-WATT, LANCASTER, LEEDS, LONDON SCHOOL OF ECONOMICS, LOUGHBOROUGH, NOTTINGHAM, OXFORD, SOUTHAMPTON, ST ANDREWS, STRATHCLYDE, UNIVERSITY COLLEGE LONDON, WARWICK
Please check with your university careers service for full details of local events.

MINIMUM ENTRY REQUIREMENTS
Relevant degree required for some roles.

APPLICATION DEADLINE
Varies by function

FURTHER INFORMATION
www.Top100GraduateEmployers.com
Register now for the latest news, events information and graduate recruitment details for Britain's leading employers.

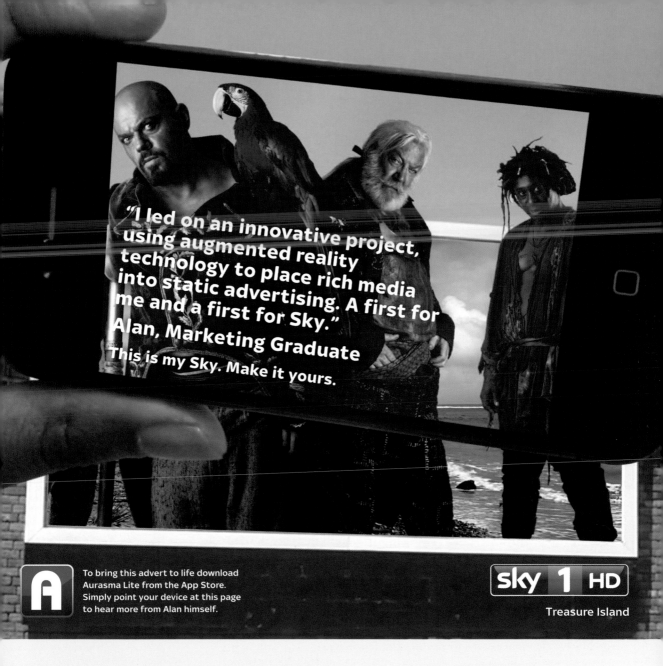

"I led on an innovative project, using augmented reality technology to place rich media into static advertising. A first for me and a first for Sky."

Alan, Marketing Graduate

This is my Sky. Make it yours.

To bring this advert to life download Aurasma Lite from the App Store. Simply point your device at this page to hear more from Alan himself.

sky **1** HD

Treasure Island

UK Graduate Programmes

You'll have the chance to shine in whatever area you choose:

Customer Operations   **Finance & Strategy**
Human Resources   **Marketing & Media**
Supply Chain & Procurement   **Technology**

To start writing your own story, go to
skygraduates.com

Believe in better

It's our people that make Sky the UK's leading entertainment company. That's why we work hard to be an inclusive employer, so everyone at Sky can be their best.

SLAUGHTER AND MAY

GRADUATE VACANCIES IN 2013

LAW

NUMBER OF VACANCIES
90 graduate jobs
For training contracts starting in 2015.

LOCATIONS OF VACANCIES

STARTING SALARY FOR 2013
£38,000

UNIVERSITY VISITS IN 2012-13
ABERDEEN, BIRMINGHAM, BRISTOL,
CAMBRIDGE, DUBLIN, DURHAM,
EDINBURGH, EXETER, GLASGOW, LEEDS,
LONDON, MANCHESTER, NEWCASTLE,
NOTTINGHAM, OXFORD, SHEFFIELD,
ST ANDREWS, WARWICK, YORK
*Please check with your university careers
service for full details of local events.*

MINIMUM ENTRY REQUIREMENTS
2.1 Degree

APPLICATION DEADLINE
See website for full details.

FURTHER INFORMATION
www.Top100GraduateEmployers.com
*Register now for the latest news, events
information and graduate recruitment
details for Britain's leading employers.*

Slaughter and May is a leading international law firm whose principle areas of practice are in the fields of corporate, commercial and financing law. The firm's clients range from leading multinationals to Premier League football clubs to venture capital start-ups.

Slaughter and May have offices in London, Brussels, Hong Kong and Beijing. They also work closely with leading independent law firms around the world – these are their "Best Friend" firms. They work in seamless integrated teams with the best lawyers around the world. This flexibility enables them to work with their clients' choice of legal advisers and always select the lawyers most appropriate for the matter in hand. They constantly review their cross-border relationships to ensure that they meet their clients' needs.

They have an extensive practice providing a full range of business legal services and expertise in all key industry sectors. Their core practice areas are Mergers and Acquisitions, Corporate and Commercial, and Financing. They also have leading practitioners in specialist areas including Tax, Competition, Dispute Resolution, Real Estate, Pensions and Employment, Financial Regulation, Information Technology and Intellectual Property.

During the two-year training contract, trainee solicitors gain experience of a broad cross-section of the firm's practice by taking an active part in the work of four or five groups, sharing an office with a partner or senior associate. In addition, Slaughter and May offers an extensive training programme of lectures and seminars led by experienced practitioners, along with courses involving discussion groups that cover general and specialised legal topics. Among their lawyers, 25 nationalities and over 50 different universities are represented.

TeachFirst

GRADUATE VACANCIES IN 2013

ALL SECTORS

NUMBER OF VACANCIES
1,260 graduate jobs

LOCATIONS OF VACANCIES

STARTING SALARY FOR 2013
£Competitive

UNIVERSITY VISITS IN 2012-13
BATH, BIRMINGHAM, BRISTOL, CAMBRIDGE,
CARDIFF, DURHAM, EDINBURGH, EXETER,
GLASGOW, HULL, IMPERIAL COLLEGE
LONDON, KING'S COLLEGE LONDON,
LANCASTER, LEEDS, LEICESTER, LIVERPOOL,
LONDON SCHOOL OF ECONOMICS,
LOUGHBOROUGH, MANCHESTER,
NEWCASTLE, NOTTINGHAM, OXFORD,
QUEEN MARY LONDON, READING,
ROYAL HOLLOWAY LONDON, SHEFFIELD,
SOUTHAMPTON, ST ANDREWS, SUSSEX,
TRINITY COLLEGE DUBLIN, UNIVERSITY
COLLEGE LONDON, WARWICK, YORK
*Please check with your university careers
service for full details of local events.*

MINIMUM ENTRY REQUIREMENTS
2.1 Degree
300 UCAS points

APPLICATION DEADLINE
20th March 2013

FURTHER INFORMATION
www.Top100GraduateEmployers.com
*Register now for the latest news, events
information and graduate recruitment
details for Britain's leading employers.*

The link between low family income and poor educational attainment is stronger in the UK than in almost any other developed country. Teach First believes that this is more than unfair – it's unacceptable and it can't be allowed to persist. Through Teach First, thousands of people are doing something about it and having a massive impact on young people's lives.

Teach First is an influential charity and movement for social change focusing on the damage and injustice done to young people by educational disadvantage. It provides the training and support to enable high-calibre graduates to make a real impact, transforming the life opportunities of young people in primary and secondary schools around the country. At the same time, Teach First helps graduates to dramatically enhance their own career potential and become part of a powerful network that is effecting profound change – in schools, boardrooms, government, and everywhere in between.

Teach First offers an exceptional Leadership Development Programme which includes in its first year a PGCE qualification. With high-quality training, supportive coaching and ongoing alumni opportunities, Teach First provides a unique platform of skills and experience to take forward into any future career. That's why over 80 companies, government agencies and public bodies back Teach First's ability to effect change and to develop leaders for the future.

Put simply, graduates who can engage, manage and inspire a class of young people can handle pretty well any situation in any industry. Few other options offer the same degree of genuine responsibility so early. Rarely, if ever, will graduates have the opportunity to make such a direct and important impact.

Take up the challenge; get involved, Teach First.

TeachFirst
"No child should grow up expecting to do badly"
Daniel Hall, taught science now Head of Department
CHANGE THEIR LIVES AND CHANGE YOURS
Just 16% of kids eligible for free school meals make it to university, compared to 96% from independent schools.*
Take up the challenge, get involved, Teach First.
*Sutton Trust, 2010
Teach First is a registered charity, no: 1098294
www.teachfirst.org.uk

Tesco is one of the world's largest retailers with operations in 14 countries, employing almost 520,000 people and serving millions of customers every week, but has a culture that is very down to earth. For graduates, that means opportunities on a scale that few can rival, with great support every step of the way.

Tesco may be the local store that millions of customers across the world rely on for everything from eggs to plasma tellies, but there's a whole lot more going on behind the shop front. Getting the best products and services from suppliers to customers draws on the talents of a huge range of different professionals with skills in everything from finance and marketing to purchasing and IT.

In fact, they offer graduate programmes in a total of 19 different areas: Buying; Corporate Affairs; Customer Analysis; Distribution; Finance; Human Resources; Marketing; Merchandising; Optometry; Pharmacy; Product Technology; Property; Store Management; Supply Chain; Technology Leadership; Tesco.com; Tesco.com IT; Trading Law & Technical; and UK Support Office.

As well as this sheer variety of career paths, Tesco is renowned as a place that gives graduates plenty of opportunity to progress. There's a real commitment to driving the business forward by letting people use their initiative and creative side. For graduates, that means not just great training opportunities (including professional qualifications, where relevant), but the chance to put what they've learnt into practice in real business situations.

As well as a good degree in any discipline, graduates need strong analytical skills and bags of ambition. Tesco looks for great team players who look to develop themselves and support others in doing a great job for their customers. Hard workers who enjoy the idea of joining a fast-paced, rapidly-changing business will thrive there.

GRADUATE VACANCIES IN 2013
FINANCE
GENERAL MANAGEMENT
HUMAN RESOURCES
IT
LOGISTICS
MARKETING
PROPERTY
PURCHASING
RESEARCH & DEVELOPMENT
RETAILING

NUMBER OF VACANCIES
300 graduate jobs

LOCATIONS OF VACANCIES

STARTING SALARY FOR 2013
£22,000-£28,000
Plus pension, life cover, share options, and Privilege Card for staff discounts.

UNIVERSITY VISITS IN 2012-13
ASTON, BATH, BIRMINGHAM, CARDIFF, DURHAM, LEEDS, LEICESTER, LOUGHBOROUGH, MANCHESTER, NEWCASTLE, NOTTINGHAM, SHEFFIELD, SOUTHAMPTON, WARWICK
Please check with your university careers service for full details of local events.

MINIMUM ENTRY REQUIREMENTS
2.1 Degree
240 UCAS points

APPLICATION DEADLINE
Varies by function

FURTHER INFORMATION
www.Top100GraduateEmployers.com
Register now for the latest news, events information and graduate recruitment details for Britain's leading employers.

Graduate   Marketing Executive, Stores   Trade Planning Manager   Programme Manager   Head of Marketing, Telecoms

A little help today could change your tomorrow.

Graduate Leadership Programmes

With a range of outstanding leadership programmes in a variety of business areas, Tesco helps turn today's graduates into the business leaders of tomorrow. As the world's third-largest retailer, we offer opportunities to match your ambitions, whether you have a talent for technology, a head for distribution or an eye for merchandising. At Tesco, we're committed to developing your career from day one, because we know that to get where you want to go, every little helps.

To choose your graduate leadership programme, visit
www.tesco-graduates.com

19
programmes
to choose
from

TESCO | *Every little helps*

Towers Watson is a leading global professional services company that has 14,000 associates working in 169 offices across 37 countries. Towers Watson's associates help the world's largest multinational corporations tackle their key people, benefits and risk issues.

Towers Watson's mission is to contribute to their clients' success through utilising people's unique capabilities and deep expertise. Towers Watson's roots may go back more than 130 years, to the world's oldest firm of actuaries, but their vision is firmly fixed on the future. In March 2012, Fortune magazine ranked Towers Watson as number one in its industry and on its list of the World's Most Admired Companies.

Towers Watson's clients recognise the need for, and actively seek, the best ideas from the brightest minds, giving Towers Watson's consultants challenges and opportunities that are difficult to find anywhere else.

The company's Graduate Programme has been designed to challenge the imagination and creativity as well as the ability to analyse data, draw conclusions and present recommendations. The programme focuses on building technical knowledge, consulting skills and overall industry experience.

Towers Watson embraces the fact that everyone is unique, that people want to take their careers in different directions and develop at their own pace. They appreciate that goals and aspirations are going to be distinctive in each individual case. With this in mind their consultants are encouraged to work at a pace of development that suits them.

Opportunities for successful applicants exist across the company, within Actuarial Consulting, Investment Consulting, Talent & Rewards Consulting or Software Engineering.

GRADUATE VACANCIES IN 2013

CONSULTING

FINANCE

IT

NUMBER OF VACANCIES
120-130 graduate jobs

LOCATIONS OF VACANCIES

STARTING SALARY FOR 2013
£28,500-£30,500+

UNIVERSITY VISITS IN 2012-13
BATH, BIRMINGHAM, BRISTOL, CAMBRIDGE, CITY, DURHAM, EDINBURGH, EXETER, HERIOT-WATT, IMPERIAL COLLEGE LONDON, LEEDS, LONDON SCHOOL OF ECONOMICS, MANCHESTER, NOTTINGHAM, OXFORD, SHEFFIELD, SOUTHAMPTON, ST ANDREWS, TRINITY COLLEGE DUBLIN, UNIVERSITY COLLEGE DUBLIN, UNIVERSITY COLLEGE LONDON, WARWICK, YORK
Please check with your university careers service for full details of local events.

MINIMUM ENTRY REQUIREMENTS
2.2 Degree
280 UCAS points

APPLICATION DEADLINE
Varies by function
Please see website for full details.

FURTHER INFORMATION
www.Top100GraduateEmployers.com
Register now for the latest news, events information and graduate recruitment details for Britain's leading employers.

make
yourmark

At Towers Watson our associates help the world's largest multinational corporations tackle their key people, benefits and risk issues. If you have the talent and the drive, you could too.

We know we are only as good as the people we employ. If you are a goal-orientated individual with outstanding intellect and academic achievement, coupled with superb problem-solving and communication skills, then Towers Watson may be the place for you to make your mark in the business world.

Whether you join us within Actuarial Consulting, Investment Consulting, Talent and Rewards Consulting or Software Engineering you will have immediate exposure to actual client assignments. Our graduate programme is designed to challenge your imagination and creativity as well as your ability to analyse data, draw conclusions and present recommendations.

Towers Watson is an exciting place to begin your career and whatever your career aspirations, you will get the guidance and the opportunities to make your mark.

Find out more at our website: **towerswatson.com/graduate/uk**

Towers Watson is an equal opportunities employer.

towerswatson.com   **TOWERS WATSON** ⱳ

No other city on earth is as defined by its public transport as London. Its red buses, black cabs and Tube trains are among the 2012 Olympic and Paralympic Games host city's most famous icons. Responsible for virtually every mode of transport in the city, without TfL London would stand still.

The Tube map has become a design classic copied the world over; even pop stars covet high-end furniture decked out in the Underground's famous moquette seat pattern. London has long been a transport innovator, and with the 150th anniversary of the world's first underground train line being celebrated next year, the city is moving forward once again with projects designed to keep it one step ahead of the competition.

Transport for London (TfL) is at the heart of this transformation. For starters 2012 has seen the launch of an updated version of a much-loved London icon, the Routemaster bus. This lean, green hybrid machine is just one of many innovative solutions being introduced to help cut pollution in western Europe's largest city. Then there is the Emirates Air Line, a slick new cable car that zips people across the Thames between the ExCel exhibition centre and the O2 Arena.

TfL's contribution to the changing face of London continues underground, with the introduction of new air-conditioned trains and upgraded stations. Work is also under way on Crossrail, a state-of-the-art underground line that will slash journey times between east and west London. The project is so vast that an academy is being set up dedicated to schooling the next generation of tunnelling experts. Whether graduates want to dig, design, plan, manage or explore corporate finance, TfL offers a unique chance to get involved with shaping the transport infrastructure of one of the world's most dynamic cities.

GRADUATE VACANCIES IN 2013
ACCOUNTANCY
ENGINEERING
FINANCE
GENERAL MANAGEMENT
IT
LOGISTICS
PURCHASING

NUMBER OF VACANCIES
Around 100 graduate jobs

LOCATIONS OF VACANCIES

STARTING SALARY FOR 2013
£25,000

UNIVERSITY VISITS IN 2012-13
ASTON, BATH, BIRMINGHAM, BRISTOL, BRUNEL, CAMBRIDGE, CITY, DURHAM, IMPERIAL COLLEGE LONDON, KING'S COLLEGE LONDON, LEEDS, LIVERPOOL, LOUGHBOROUGH, MANCHESTER, NEWCASTLE, NOTTINGHAM, QUEEN MARY LONDON, READING, SHEFFIELD, SOUTHAMPTON, SURREY, UNIVERSITY COLLEGE LONDON, WARWICK
Please check with your university careers service for full details of local events.

MINIMUM ENTRY REQUIREMENTS
2.1 Degree

APPLICATION DEADLINE
Varies by function

FURTHER INFORMATION
www.Top100GraduateEmployers.com
Register now for the latest news, events information and graduate recruitment details for Britain's leading employers.

Leave your mark on London—become a TfL graduate

Take a wider look at tfl.gov.uk/graduates

We want to be as diverse as the city we represent and welcome applications from everyone regardless of age, gender, ethnicity, sexual orientation, faith or disability.

MAYOR OF LONDON

Transport for London

UBS draws on its 150-year heritage to serve private, institutional and corporate clients worldwide, as well as retail clients in Switzerland. The firm combines its wealth management, investment banking and asset management businesses with its Swiss operations to deliver superior financial solutions.

UBS recruits graduates from all academic backgrounds – the humanities and sciences, as well as economics and finance. Because of its global reach, the firm is particularly keen to hear from students with strong language skills. For UBS, degree subject is less important than a graduate's ability to prove they can analyse problems, plan ahead, make decisions, demonstrate sound judgement, and communicate with others. The other qualities UBS seeks in graduates are ambition, integrity, a commitment to accuracy, and a desire to work collaboratively with other friendly but driven professionals.

UBS's Graduate Training Program offers talented graduates 18-24 months of continuous learning in a fast-paced but supportive environment. The program lays the foundation for a rewarding career in finance by combining intensive classroom education, coaching from more senior colleagues and on-the-job experience in a variety of teams.

UBS is a place where graduates can expect to be stretched long after university. As a global business, the firm offers a world of opportunities for successful applicants to develop their talent – and to be recognised and rewarded for it. As well as gaining hands-on experience as part of a smart, ambitious team, graduates will benefit from continued education so they can shape their career. Whether it's acquiring the technical knowledge to create the products of the future or developing the skills to be one of UBS's leaders of tomorrow, graduates will always be encouraged to make the most of their talents.

GRADUATE VACANCIES IN 2013
ACCOUNTANCY
FINANCE
HUMAN RESOURCES
INVESTMENT BANKING
IT

NUMBER OF VACANCIES
300+ graduate jobs

LOCATIONS OF VACANCIES

Vacancies also available in Europe, the USA and Asia.

STARTING SALARY FOR 2013
£Competitive

UNIVERSITY VISITS IN 2012-13
ASTON, BATH, BRISTOL, CAMBRIDGE, CITY, IMPERIAL COLLEGE LONDON, LONDON SCHOOL OF ECONOMICS, LOUGHBOROUGH, MANCHESTER, NOTTINGHAM, OXFORD, WARWICK
Please check with your university careers service for full details of local events.

MINIMUM ENTRY REQUIREMENTS
2.1 Degree
300 UCAS points

APPLICATION DEADLINE
Varies by function

FURTHER INFORMATION
www.Top100GraduateEmployers.com
Register now for the latest news, events information and graduate recruitment details for Britain's leading employers.

You know *what you want.*
We'll help you get there.

At UBS, our internship and graduate training programs are designed to be a springboard for talented students like you. If you are serious about your career and intrigued by international banking, we offer a stimulating, collaborative environment with opportunities to achieve success across many disciplines. Wherever you are in your academic career, make your future a part of ours by visiting **www.ubs.com/graduates**

UBS is an Equal Opportunity Employer. We respect and seek to empower each individual and the diverse cultures, perspectives, skills and experiences within our workforce.

We will not rest

Learn business fast

Unilever, a leading consumer goods company, makes some of the world's best loved brands: Dove, Flora, Tresemmé, Comfort, Knorr and Marmite to name a few. 150 million times a day, someone somewhere chooses a Unilever product. Unilever's products are sold in 180 countries and they employ 171,000 people globally.

Around the world, Unilever products help people look good, feel good and get more out of life. Each results from deep thought, hard work and carefully applied skills.

Unilever want graduates with the will to lead others in driving these brands forward. The Future Leaders Programme (UFLP) helps that talent reach senior management. Quickly.

Graduates can apply to one of the following areas – Financial Management, Supply Chain Management, Customer Management (Sales), Human Resources, Business & Technology Management, Research & Development, Marketing, China Programme and Unilever's Asia, Middle East, Africa & Russia (AMEAR) Programme. Whichever area graduates join, they'll learn business fast.

The two to three year programme (depending on the business area) involves placements across Unilever's UK & Ireland business with responsibility from day one, alongside excellent training in leadership and business. The company will support successful applicants in achieving Chartered status and qualifications such as CIMA, IMechE, IChemE, IEE, APICS, ICS and CIPD. When the programme ends, they will move into a management role.

Unilever's challenge? To develop ways of working that double its size, while reducing its environmental impact by 2020. Behind that ambition, and every brand, lie exciting challenges.

GRADUATE VACANCIES IN 2013

ENGINEERING
FINANCE
HUMAN RESOURCES
IT
LOGISTICS
MARKETING
RESEARCH & DEVELOPMENT
SALES

NUMBER OF VACANCIES
60-70 graduate jobs

LOCATIONS OF VACANCIES

Vacancies also available in Asia and elsewhere in the world.

STARTING SALARY FOR 2013
£29,000
Plus a performance-related bonus every year and a salary increase every 6 months.

UNIVERSITY VISITS IN 2012-13
ASTON, BATH, BIRMINGHAM, BRISTOL, CAMBRIDGE, DURHAM, IMPERIAL COLLEGE LONDON, LANCASTER, LEEDS, LIVERPOOL, LOUGHBOROUGH, MANCHESTER, NEWCASTLE, NOTTINGHAM, OXFORD, SHEFFIELD, SURREY, UNIVERSITY COLLEGE LONDON, WARWICK
Please check with your university careers service for full details of local events.

MINIMUM ENTRY REQUIREMENTS
2.2 Degree
300 UCAS points
Relevant degree required for some roles.

APPLICATION DEADLINE
Please see website for full details.

FURTHER INFORMATION
www.Top100GraduateEmployers.com
Register now for the latest news, events information and graduate recruitment details for Britain's leading employers.

Hate Marmite? Love business.

Far more than an iconic spread, Marmite is a powerful way to learn business fast.

It's driving the progress of a market-leading brand. It's working with experts in Financial Management, Customer Management (Sales), Human Resources and Supply Chain Management to delight millions of customers. It's tapping into continuous business mentoring, excellent training, and dealing with surprising challenges every day.

It's fast, it's exciting, it's not for the faint-hearted. It's not just Marmite – it's the Unilever Future Leaders Programme.

Learn business fast:
www.unilever.co.uk/graduates
www.facebook.com/unilevercareers

WPP

GRADUATE VACANCIES IN 2013
MARKETING
MEDIA

NUMBER OF VACANCIES
1-10 graduate jobs

LOCATIONS OF VACANCIES

STARTING SALARY FOR 2013
£Competitive

UNIVERSITY VISITS IN 2012-13
BRISTOL, CAMBRIDGE, LONDON SCHOOL
OF ECONOMICS, OXFORD
*Please check with your university careers
service for full details of local events.*

MINIMUM ENTRY REQUIREMENTS
2.1 Degree

APPLICATION DEADLINE
8th November 2012
12.00 GMT.

FURTHER INFORMATION
www.Top100GraduateEmployers.com
*Register now for the latest news, events
information and graduate recruitment
details for Britain's leading employers.*

WPP is the world leader in communications services, with over 150 companies setting industry standards in advertising; media investment management; consumer insight; public relations & public affairs; branding & identity; healthcare communications; direct, digital, promotion & relationship marketing; and specialist communications.

WPP companies work with many of the world's leading brands, creating communications ideas that help to build business. Their clients include 344 of the Fortune Global 500; all of the Dow Jones 30; 63 of the NASDAQ 100; and 33 of the Fortune e-50. The Group also works with 359 clients across six or more countries. Collectively, WPP employs 158,000 people (including associates) in 2,500 offices in 108 countries.

WPP Marketing Fellowships develop high-calibre management talent with unique experience across a range of marketing disciplines. Over three years, Fellows work in three different WPP operating companies, each representing a different marketing communications discipline and geography. Each rotation is chosen on the basis of the individual's interests and the Group's needs.

Fellowships will be awarded to applicants who are intellectually curious and motivated by the prospect of delivering high-quality communications services to their clients. WPP wants people who are committed to marketing communications, take a rigorous and creative approach to problem-solving, are intellectually curious and will function well in a flexible, loosely structured work environment.

WPP is offering several three-year Fellowships, with competitive remuneration and excellent long term career prospects within WPP. Many former Fellows now occupy senior management positions in WPP companies across the world.